D1484811

# THE NEW SCIENCE OF THE SPIRIT

# THE NEW SCIENCE
## OF THE SPIRIT

DAVID   ASH

The College of Psychic Studies
16 Queensberry Place, London SW7 2EB

Copyright © David Ash 1995

First published in 1995 by
The College of Psychic Studies
16 Queensberry Place, London, SW7 2EB

All rights reserved. No part of this
publication may be reproduced, stored
in a retrieval system, transmitted in
any form or by any means electronic,
mechanical, recording or photocopying,
or otherwise, without prior permission
from the publishers, except for
brief quotations embodied in
literary articles or reviews.

British Library Cataloguing-in-Publication Data

A catalogue record of this book
is available from The British Library
ISBN 0 903336 55 3

Typeset by The Local Press, Totnes, Devon.
Printed and bound in Great Britain
by Whitstable Litho, Whitstable, Kent

# CONTENTS

# ACKNOWLEDGEMENTS

First I would like to remember my father, the late Dr Michael Ash, who taught me that even if I stand alone against the entire world it does not mean that I am wrong.

Next I would like to thank Peter Hewitt. Whilst he didn't work with me on this book he spent six months with me on an earlier, unpublished version. Peter gave me immense support and encouragement in my work, drawing my attention to the information which led me to question the validity of the uncertainty principle and credit must be given to him for my understanding of the neutrino.

I am very grateful to Brian Kitt and Will Manwearing for their help with printing early versions of this work and my daughters Josephine and Jessica who made it possible for me to write the book by providing me with a word processor. I have Vincent to thank for Bess, the Bedford truck he converted into the home and sanctuary in which the first drafts of this book were written. I am very grateful to Ricky Liew, Jessie and Chin of Selangor, Malasia, for their generosity in printing copies of an early version of this book.

I thank all those scientists who have read my work, bringing my attention to mistakes and misunderstandings which needed correction, especially Bert Nathan and John Coles and I take this opportunity to thank all those who have helped me, over thirty years, to develop my science; all those who have helped me to set up lectures and seminars, prepare my books and network my work, most especially André Dufour and Jacquline Longstaff. I wish to thank my first wife, Anna and Sir George Trevelyan for their encouragement and support over many years, Lord Northampton for giving me the clue to understanding nuclear energy and Nigel Blair who supported me with his library and network and suggested the title for this book. I am also grateful to Ellen Stilwell for the foundation of the University of Light. I appreciate the patience and support of Keith and Judith of the Local Press and Alison of Dartington Tech. I am especially grateful to Dudley Poplak of the College of Psychic Studies for publishing this book and Ben Grafton for his help with the editing. My special love and thanks go to my second wife Heather, who did a major edit and gave me continual love and support. Finally, I would like to acknowledge Hermes and Soltec, the inspirations behind my works.

# LIST OF FIGURES

# PREFACE

*"If you want to promote the growth of scientific knowledge, you should adopt the method of extravagant guess followed by unrestrained criticism in which the guesses found to be false are cast from the body of science."*

*Karl Popper*

I have written *The New Science of the Spirit* for men and women everywhere who are striving to understand underlying realities and reconcile science with the spirit. Throughout this century, the gap between science and spirit has widened. Most scientists have either debunked metaphysics and mysticism or treated them with utter contempt. Things psychic or supernatural have been explained away and undeniable paranormal phenomena have been completely ignored. Therefore, before I attempt to bridge the gap it is necessary for me to question the existing theories in physics. As my father said, "Before you give them a nut to crack, crack their nut."

It has been my lifelong ambition to crack the nut of materialism and in the first chapter of this book I launch a torpedo at modern materialistic science. I am not directing a personal attack against scientists, though some may feel offended by what I have to say and the way I say it. I am attempting to sink the *Bismark* of materialism that threatens many new ideas and alternative approaches that are being launched on the oceans of human understanding.

Most scientists think that scientific materialism was banished at the beginning of the 20th century but, as I point out in the second chapter, this is not so. Materialism has disguised itself in quantum thinking and shrouded itself in uncertainty and I am determined that science should be rid of this fundamental error.

However, this book isn't written primarily for scientists, it is more for those seeking a place for science in the 'New Age'. In the New Age movement people are talking about higher consciousness, other dimensions, getting in touch with the higher-self and ascension. My objective has been to create a new scientific framework of understanding to make these ideas more credible for people in the mainstream of orthodox thinking.

Many are inclined to dismiss the New Age movement as unscientific. *The New Science of the Spirit* offers a scientific foundation for the New Age movement. It is a new metaphysics, born out of modern physics which leads science toward the spirit and brings the spirit back into science. It is also a radical approach to theoretical physics which challenges uncertain theories and inflexible attitudes in science. To quote Sir Fred Hoyle, from *The Observer*, September 18, 1994, "In the past, the truly great ideas were the radical ones that offended people. Today we could not get them past the grant application stage. We are now suffocating our best young minds. Our science is becoming hopelessly dull."

I have never applied for a grant nor allowed my mind to be suffocated. My approach to science, like my life, has never been dull. I take this opportunity to share my approach to science with you and I hope you enjoy it as much as I have, over the last thirty years it has preoccupied my attention.

*David Ash, Totnes, Devon 1995*

# INTRODUCTION

*"If we do discover a complete theory, it should in time be understandable in broad principle by everyone, not just a few scientists. Then we should all, philosophers, scientists, and just ordinary people, be able to take part in the discussion of the question of why it is that we and the universe exist. If we find the answer to that, it would be the ultimate triumph of human reason - for then we would know the mind of God."*

*Stephen Hawking*

In this book I have endeavoured to establish the basis for a new world view. In an ideal world there would be as many world views as there are people because everyone would be thinking for themselves. I am one of those people who are not happy to allow others to do their thinking for them. I have to think things out for myself and I have taken a lot of trouble to think about the Universe. The result is a view of the Universe, developed by a layman for laymen and women.

A major objective of my work is to simplify and unify physics. In my approach to the subject I have not attempted to meet up to the rigorous standards of modern physics because I don't believe that truth will be wrung out of the Universe by the exacting demands of professional scientists. Science cannot prove what is true, but it can expose what is false. I appreciate it when scientists point out the flaws in my work - as I have pointed out what I perceive to be flaws in existing physics. Criticism is necessary to burn away the dross and uncover the truth because like gold, the truth will survive the heat of a furnace, and be separated from falsehoods which exist, like fool's gold, as pretenders to truth. The truth endures. It does not have to be proved because it cannot be disproved. It can be denied but never destroyed and will always emerge like green shoots from the grass roots. Truth can come through any mind as a free flight of imagination and whilst fanciful inspirations need to be tested against scientific observations, excessive rigour usually characterises an entrenched and unimaginative mind which feels threatened by imaginative thinking.

Whilst I welcome constructive criticism, I am aware that new ideas are almost invariably resisted because people with a vested interest in the established order fear change. It is Russell's law that: *The resistance to new ideas increases by the square of their importance.* James Gleick spoke of the "...ferocious resistance from traditional quarters" to the revolutionary chaos theory in its early days and James Watson described the opponents to the DNA theory as, "...cantankerous fools who unfailingly backed the wrong horses".

However, there is nothing more powerful than an idea whose time has arrived. It will win through regardless of opposition. Criticism will strengthen it and controversy will help it to spread.

An open-minded scientist will welcome fresh approaches. People who react to new ideas reveal that they are not real scientists. Rather than think for themselves, they accept as true whatever it is they have been taught and resist people with original thoughts. As Gary Zukav explains, in *The Dancing Wu Li Masters*, "...it is possible that scientists, poets, painters and writers are all members of the same family of people whose gift it is by nature to take those things which we call commonplace and to re-present them to us in such ways that our self-imposed limitations are expanded. Those people in whom this gift is especially pronounced, we call geniuses."

"The fact is that most 'scientists' are technicians. They are not interested in the essentially new. Their field of vision is relatively narrow; their energies are directed toward applying what is already known. Because their noses often are buried in the bark of a particular tree, it is difficult to speak meaningfully to them of forests."

True scientists entertain new ideas because they are new. Technicians will resist new ideas for precisely the same reason. If they can't refute a new approach they will ignore it. This occurred when David Bohm's theory of the Implicate Order couldn't be dismissed. In his book *Unravelling the Mind of God*, Robert Matthews said that when Oppenheimer - father of the atom bomb - looked at Bohm's fresh approach to the quantum theory, he commented, "Well, we can't find anything wrong with it so we will just have to ignore it."

I have no doubt I will be treated as a heretic and my work will meet with opposition because it is a completely unorthodox approach to quantum physics, not only in the new ideas it presents, but in the way they are presented. In my approach to physics I have turned my back on mathematics. I have done this for a number of very good reasons.

Physics has endless mathematical formulae to show how things in our world work but little knowledge of what they are. Science, in the study of natural phenomena, has been more concerned with the description and exploitation of nature than to provide a fundamental understanding of it. It has not been necessary for scientists to know what things are in order to know how they work  Scientists need to know how electricity works in order to harness it but, even today, few scientists can claim to know what electrical energy is.

Early scientists were more concerned to understand nature than exploit it. They were more interested in developing a coherent world view than a new technology. This was certainly the case with Michael Faraday. Faraday pioneered electricity in order to gain a deeper insight into the world in which we live. His discovery of the rudimentary principles of electro-magnetism was the consequence rather than the objective of his search.

In his endeavour to understand the nature of electric and magnetic forces, Faraday developed a simple model of lines of force. This model was subsequently developed by James Clerk Maxwell in a mathematical form. Few theories in science have been as enduring as Maxwell's electro-magnetic theory and few models as successful as Faraday's lines of force. Faraday and Maxwell established a clear precedent in science for the presentation of a non-mathematical model, which is subsequently developed in a mathematical form.

Men of vision are not always mathematicians and breakthroughs come more often from minds capable of imaginative thinking, than minds which follow logical disciplines and consensus thoughtforms - true genius lies more in original thought than exceptionally high I.Q. New insights lead to new equations, so original thinking should come before mathematics.

I believe physics has been drowned in mathematics. As Gary Zukav said: "The fact is that physics is not mathematics...Stripped of mathematics, physics becomes pure enchantment."

For me physics is pure enchantment and for what I wish to achieve, mathematics is a positive disadvantage. I am attempting to explain the fundamental nature of things, not describe their actions. Whilst my new world view may eventually receive mathematical treatment, at present I want to reach a far larger audience than just mathematicians and physicists.

Stephen Hawking concluded his book, *A Brief History of Time*, with the statement: "If we do discover a complete theory, it should in time be understandable in broad principle by everyone, not just a few scientists..." To achieve this end, such a 'complete theory' would have to be presented in a non-mathematical form so that ordinary people could understand it. What good is a world view unless it can be communicated to the world at large? In the words of Erwin Schrödinger, "If you cannot - in the long run - tell everyone what you have been doing, your doing has been worthless."

I believe it is a greater achievement to present a complex idea in simple language than impenetrable mathematical formulae. I have spent my whole life simplifying my work. The last thing I want to do is bog it down with equations - especially as I am addressing my ideas to ordinary people rather than trained scientists. Lord Rutherford, who expressed his momentous discoveries in utmost simplicity, said: "These fundamental things have got to be simple," and Feynman said: "It is simple therefore it is beautiful...This is common to all our laws; they all turn out to be simple things, although complex in their actual actions."

Physics is not the simplest of subjects but a fundamental understanding of the Universe is very empowering and important at this time because I firmly believe that it is science, rather than religion, that will lead mankind back to God. Science has a deep prejudice against the idea of God and the possibility that religious, supernatural, psychic or spiritual phenomena may be real. In the early days of science this attitude was important to release mankind from the bondage of religious fear and superstition. Even today scientific thinking has an important role to play in protecting us from a lot of superstitious nonsense which less discerning minds are prone to believe. However, the pendulum has swung too far when, in the name of science, everything psychic, supernatural, mystical or paranormal is dismissed out of hand.

Andrew Harvey, an Oxford scholar and explorer of the spiritual realm summarised the attitude of many university academics and scientists to mysticism when he quoted a colleague saying that "only scientific criteria for truth are valuable and mystics are pathological cases."

My work is based on a discovery I made from the mystical tradition of India. Far from being pathological cases, I believe that mystics may have discovered the key to the Universe, and done this through pure mystical insight rather than scientific investigation. I do not want to deny the value of science or underestimate the vision and dedication of many great scientists. Certainly, I believe that most of what science has to teach us is valid and the contribution of science to our understanding of the Universe is undeniable. However, in the development of a nuclear weapons technology for maximum assured destruction, it has to be admitted that it is science rather than mysticism which is displaying pathological symptoms. I believe that science in denial of spirit is destroying the world and the way forward is not science in opposition to mysticism but science in harmony with mysticism. I applaud the efforts of those scientists and mystics who meet in order to find common ground and I have the utmost respect for mystical physicists. Mysticism could rescue science from materialism and the endemic cynicism that is destroying society and the Earth. In the attempt to deny the existence of God and the unseen worlds of spirit, I believe materialistic scientists merely highlight the hopelessness of their world view.

As a child, I declared that I was going to prove the existence of God through science. However, I now appreciate that science can neither prove nor disprove the existence of God. Science can only provide us with a way of studying the fascinating universe in which we live. However, the realisation that everything is formed out of energy shows that it is materialism rather than God which should be proclaimed as dead. Materialism should have died at the beginning of the twentieth century. Instead it has spread like cancer throughout 20th-century science and the so-called New Physics is riddled with it. I am determined to cut it out by revealing what I perceive to be myths in modern physics.

Chapter 1

# THE MYTHS IN
# MODERN
# PHYSICS

*"We are all agreed that your theory is crazy. The question which divides us, is whether it is crazy enough."*

*Niels Bohr*

On April 29, 1980, Stephen Hawking was inaugurated as Lucasian Professor of Mathematics at Cambridge. In his Inaugural Lecture entitled, *'Is the end in sight for theoretical physics?'* he discussed the possibility that the goal of theoretical physics might be achieved in the not too-distant future: say by the end of the century.

Many scientists today believe that, by the end of the 20th century, science will be in sight of a complete understanding of the Universe and no new major discoveries should be expected in future physics. Scientists expressed the same view at the end of the 19th century. Except for 'two small clouds on the horizon', scientists thought they had solved all the problems. No new basic discoveries were expected and the future work in physics was believed to lie in improved methods of measurement to the sixth decimal place. The two small clouds - the result of the Michelson-Morley experiment and the photoelectric effect - grew into hurricanes, which swept away the theories of 19th-century physics and led to quantum theory and the theories of relativity.

History is about to repeat itself. Once again, two small clouds have appeared on the scientific horizon which threaten a storm that could blow away the major theories for particles and forces which have become established in 20th-century physics. These clouds concern the structure of the proton and the neutron, two naturally occurring particles in the nucleus of the atom.

Most physicists believe that protons and neutrons are made of quarks. On the 27th January 1977, BBC Television broadcast a report on the new physics in a programme entitled, *The Key to the Universe*. In the companion book to this programme, under the same title, Nigel Calder wrote about how the theory for quarks originated:

"In the early 1930's the contents of the Universe seemed simple. From just three kinds of particles, electrons, protons and neutrons you could make every material object known at the time. Thirty years later human beings were confronted with a bewildering jumble of dozens of heavy, apparently elementary particles, mostly very short lived. They came to light either in the cosmic rays or in experiments with the accelerators. The particles had various mass-energies and differing qualities such as electric charge, spin, lifetimes and so forth. Moreover they were given confusing, mostly Greek names so that one of the most eminent of physicists, Enrico Fermi, was driven to remark before his death in 1954, 'If I could remember the names of all these particles I would have been a botanist'.

"The proliferation could be understood, to some extent, in that many of the particles seemed to be energetic relatives of the proton. Because they possessed greater inherent energy their masses were greater. Each was in some sense less tightly bound together than a proton and it could quickly change into a proton with a release of binding energy and an associated loss of mass. But that implied the proton was not a truly basic particle: it was made of something else which could be bound more or less tightly together.

"A small group of theorists brought order out of chaos. The

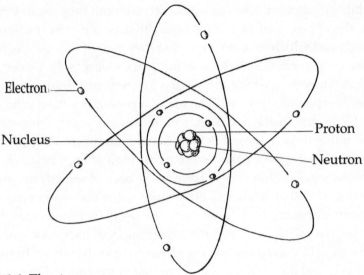

*Fig. 1.1 The atom*

principal figure amongst them was Murray Gell-Mann of the California Institute of Technology, then in his early thirties. He declared that all the heavy particles of nature were made out of three kinds of quarks. He had the word from a phrase of James Joyce, 'Three quarks for Muster Mark'. It was the mocking cry of gulls which Gell-Mann took as referring to quarts of beer, so he pronounced quark to rhyme with 'stork'. Many other physicists rhymed it with 'Mark'. In German, as sceptics were not slow to notice, 'quark' meant cream cheese or nonsense..."

There is a lot in a name and the quark theory is nonsense, as the name suggests, not because of mocking gulls but because of a black swan. The Austrian philosopher, Karl Popper, used an analogy of black and white swans to explain that science is not in the business of proving theories but rather of disproving them. Someone could have a theory that all swans are white but even if a thousand white swans were counted, their belief would not be proved and the addition of more white swans wouldn't make it any more true. However, the appearance of a single black swan would disprove the theory altogether. Scientific theories are white swan belief systems which survive until they are destroyed by the appearance of a black swan, that is, the arrival of even a single fact which makes it clear that they cannot be true. As far as I am concerned, the black swan for quark theory is the proton.

A single fact which throws the quark theory into question is the life-span of a proton. The life of a proton has been estimated at $10^{33}$ years, that is a billion, trillion, trillion years, whereas one ten billionth of a second is considered a strangely long life-span for any of the new particles found in high energy research. As spontaneous proton decays have never been observed, the proton can be treated as being infinitely more stable than any of the new, heavy particles that have come to light in the accelerators. Physicists call the heavy particles *baryons* from the Greek word for heavy. They account for the difference in life-span between protons and other baryons in a law called the law of *Conservation of Baryon numbers*. However, this law doesn't tell us why protons live for so much longer than the other particles, it simply states, mathematically, that they do so. It is just one of the many instances in science where a statement is made that phenomena are observed to behave in a certain way, but no reason is given for why this is so.

With over 31 million seconds in a year, the difference between the estimated life-span of a proton and one of the new particles is a figure in excess of $3 \times 10^{50}$ (3 with fifty zeros behind it). Mathematicians use the number $10^{50}$ as a cut-off point for probability. If the probability of something happening is less than 1 in $10^{50}$ then scientists are forced to accept that it never occurs. With a difference in stability in excess of $10^{50}$, it can be argued that it is beyond the bounds of probability that protons should be of similar structure to other baryons, unless a very good reason is given for the disparity in their lifespans.

This point is obvious from a simple analogy of building sites. Imagine you are walking down a road between two building sites. On the site to the left, the houses are so shoddy they disintegrate as soon as they are built. Within a fraction of a second of the last lick of paint being applied, they vanish. On the site to the right, however, the houses are very well built, so much so that they are advertised for sale with a trillion-year guarantee. Surely it would be crazy to assume that the same bricks, mortar and construction techniques are employed on both building sites. There would have to be some difference in the building methods and materials employed on the two sites to account for the difference in the durability of the houses.

The baryon particles are like houses in this analogy. The six different types of quark are equivalent to bricks and the gluon bonds, which bind them together, are equivalent to the mortar. Scientists who believe the quark theory accept that different combinations of three quark bricks, cemented together with gluon bonds, give rise to all the heavy particles, including protons and neutrons, without explaining why protons are infinitely more durable than the others.

I contend that quarks could be used to explain protons, or they could be used to account for the other baryons, but not both! To use quark theory to explain only protons would be pointless, because the theory was invented to explain the new baryons. But if quark theory provided an explanation for all the baryons apart from the proton, it would still be pointless because the great bulk of the mass of the Universe consists of protons, whereas the other baryons - apart from the neutron - have been observed only in high energy experiments. If the theory were to exclude protons, the entire world-wide programme of high energy research, which dominates physics, would be meaningless.

Physicists talk about discovering new particles of matter in the high energy research, but to say they have been discovered is misleading, because discovery implies that something already exists and is waiting to be found. The short-lived baryons have been created out of the massive amounts of energy, fed into the high energy particle accelerators. These new heavy particles, synthesised in the accelerators, have no place in normal matter. They are just products of high energy research. Research is meaningless if it deals only with anomalies of the experiments and not with the realities existing in the world outside the laboratory.

During World War II, physicists succeeded in harnessing the energy locked in the atom to make the most terrible weapons of destruction ever known to mankind. Since then they have been endowed with virtually unlimited budgets for continued nuclear research. Vast sums of money have been spent on building and running massive particle accelerators. Using these, they created a host of new particles which were explained by the quark theory. The theory threw up new difficulties and exciting predictions which required more research and more powerful accelerators. Each nation, or group of developed nations, wanting to be at the forefront of discovery, was only too happy to spend the equivalent of the gross national product of poorer nations on a bigger and better accelerator than the 'nation next door'.

Whilst everything in the world is supposed to be made of quarks, not a single quark has ever been observed in a free state - even though no expense or effort has been spared, over the last thirty years, to try and find one. Intent 'to throw good billions after bad', the Americans were going to spend upwards of $8 billion on the biggest accelerator in the world. Sprawling in Texas - the new *Superconducting Supercollider* was going to be 86 kilometres in circumference - this monster machine would have been twenty times more powerful than any working today. Its main purpose was to further research into quarks and force-carrying particles. Creating a new generation of particles, this accelerator would have led to more elaborations on the theories, which would require more research and eventually the need for a even bigger accelerator. Fortunately the plans to build the Texas giant have been shelved, because to prove the predictions of GUT - the *Grand Unified-field Theory* - scientists would need an accelerator as big as the solar system. High energy research has threatened an endless cycle in which research physicists create problems for theoretical physicists to solve and they, in turn, predict yet more problems to research. Whilst this elaborate game ensures indefinite employment for scientists and their army of technicians, it produces information which is of little relevance or value to the tax payers who have to foot the enormous bill.

*...In a sad world of homeless and starving people there once lived a mad professor who believed in flying pigs. No one had ever seen a flying pig but the mad professor managed to convince all the Universities, in his world, that hunting for flying pigs was the most valuable line of research they could undertake. As the greatest minds in the nutty world caught flying pig fever, the developed nations fell over themselves in the frenzy to build bigger and ever more powerful cannons for blasting at flying pigs. No expense was spared. Money taken from the people, which could have been used to improve the quality of their lives, was squandered in the search, but after decades of hunting no one spotted a single flying pig - even though from the debris descending from the sky, boffins deduced they had bagged the top porker. You would have thought that eventually the learned professors would admit that their flying pig theory was cranky, but not willing to be thought of as cranks, they just went on building ever more elaborate hunting.apparatus.*

*Another nut case, in that crazy world, was the mad professor of puddings! A student in his department of nutrition baked plums in a pudding, then ran round shouting, "Eureka, I have just invented plum pudding!"*

*The professor was not impressed. He snorted over his spectacles, "That is not a plum pudding. That is a Blackforest gâteau."*

*"But," argued the downcast student, "I mixed plums into my pudding before I baked it and when I weighed it, the weight was that of the plums and the pud and at the end, when I shook the pudding, out came a plum. It has to be a plum pudding!"*

*The professor became really angry. "You stupid student, have you learnt nothing of what I have taught you? When you bake plums in a pudding the ingredients completely change their identity. Due to the interaction of a weak cooking force, the plums change into cherries and the pudding becomes a Blackforest gâteau."*

*"Well, how do you explain the plum that fell out of the pudding?"*
*retorted the student, "there are no plums in a Blackforest gâteau."*

*"The gâteau is unstable," replied the professor, "after a few minutes*
*it falls apart into its original ingredients - plums and pudding."*

*How could the student argue? He was speaking to none other than*
*the President of the Royal Society of Puddings. If he wanted to make it*
*in his world and get a good career in the cake and pudding industry, he*
*had to accept that a pudding full of plums was a Blackforest gâteau...*

If you think that modern science is sane, then I suggest you think
again. Electrons are very light and bear a negative charge. They
could be likened to the plums in the story. Protons bear a positive
charge and are 1836 times as massive as electrons. They could be
likened to the pudding mass. (In physics, the proton is
considered to be smaller that the electron, however, the proton is
greater than the electron in mass-energy and it is the greater mass
and inertia of the proton, rather than its size, which would enable
it to bind an electron.) The neutron is neutral in charge and can
be formed out of an electron and proton in a process called *K-
capture*. The neutron has slightly more than the sum mass of an
electron and proton and in a process called *beta decay*, it falls apart
into an electron and a proton. From this you would imagine the
neutron must be a bound state of electron and proton,
represented by the plum pudding. However, I don't recommend
you suggest this to a professor of physics. He would think you
are quite stupid to jump to that obvious conclusion.

"Neutrons are not electrons bound to protons," he would
insist. "The electron and proton lose their identity as they come
together to form a neutron but regain their identity again when
the unstable neutron falls apart."

If you stayed awhile to listen he might tell you that the proton
is made up of two up-quarks and one down-quark. He would
then explain that the neutron is made up of two down-quarks and
one up-quark and go on to say that when a proton interacts with
an electron, a force called the *weak nuclear force* comes into play, to

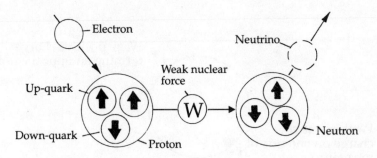

***Fig. 1.2*** *Quarks and the weak nuclear force*

transform an up-quark into a down-quark and the electron into an elusive particle called a *neutrino*. If you asked him to elaborate, he might tell you that in this process the electron and proton would have ceased to exist, their place being taken by the neutron and neutrino. If you were alarmed at this he would reassure you that they come back into existence if the process is reversed, with an anti-neutrino. However, I suggest you look for an exit sign if he begins to talk about *fermions, quantum-spin, Z* and *W particles*, and make a run for it should he begin to support his arguments with the law of *Conservation of Angular Momentum* and *Fermi-Dirac statistics*. Should you get completely lost and find yourself wondering what quark is, you should find it down at your local supermarket somewhere between the yoghurt and the cream cheese!

*Meanwhile... back in the nutrition department of the crazy world, all was not going well with the mad professor of puddings. Another student baked plums in a pudding then licked it. He tasted a plum and so established that the plums did not lose their identity when baked in a pudding. The mad professor was very embarrassed by the arrival of this awkward fact. He ranted and raved and made it a rule that food was never again to be tasted in the lab and then he used his great prestige and authority to ensure that when the result of the lick-experiment was printed in the textbooks, it was set in small type so that, hopefully, students would*

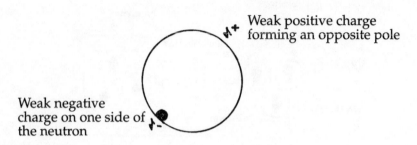

Weak positive charge
forming an opposite pole

Weak negative
charge on one side of
the neutron

**Fig. 1.3** *Electric dipole of the neutron*

*overlook it, or see it as a trivial and totally unimportant fact...*

The lick-experiment highlights the discovery of a number of awkward facts about the neutron. In 1957, Smith, Purcell and Ramsey discovered that a neutron has a slight *electric dipole moment*. This means the neutron is not entirely neutral. On one spot it displays a minute negative charge, in the order of a billion, trillion times weaker than that of a single electron. This suggests that the neutron is a bound state of opposite charges which mostly cancel each other out. (This occurs in an atom, which is electrically neutral because it contains equal numbers of oppositely charged particles.)

When first I was shown the information about the electric dipole of a neutron, it was in a short paragraph and set in small type. That aroused my suspicions. I could smell a rat. There had to be some reason why physicists were so adamant that a neutron was not an electron bound to a proton, in the face of obvious evidence to suggest that it was. The dipole moment appeared to be an awkward fact. When I came across it again, in the physics library of Exeter University, it was in a textbook on nuclei and particles, by a world authority on neutrons, Emilio Segre. Segre said the electric dipole moment of the neutron was equal to the charge on an electron $\times 10^{-20}$ (-0.1 ± 2.4) but followed with the comment, "...hence this moment could be exactly zero, in agreement with the theory". Whilst the large margin of error does not allow the 1957 measure to be taken as conclusive, the way this comment was phrased suggested to me that the Segre saw the measure as a threat to the theory and wanted it to be dismissed as a trivial and totally unimportant fact.

The presence of charged particles in the neutron is supported by the fact that the neutron has a *magnetic moment* of -1.91 nuclear magnetrons. If the neutron were a truly neutral particle, it should have no magnetic moment whatsoever because the magnetism of a particle is created by the spin of its charge. A particle cannot have a magnetic moment unless it has a charge. The magnetism of a neutron adds support to the view that it is a bound state of two opposite charges which mostly cancel each other out rather than a single particle with no charge at all.

Another piece of evidence to support the view that in a neutron electrons are bound to a specific site on the proton came from a discovery made in 1956 by the American physicist Chien Shiung Wu. Wu lined up the nuclei of radioactive atoms in a magnetic field so they were all spinning in the same direction and observed that more electrons were emitted in one direction than in another. This experiment showed that in beta decay electrons are emitted directionally as if they emerged from a specific site on a neutron.

There is overwhelming evidence to support the view that an electron is bound to a proton to form a neutron. Against this, physicists argue that a neutron has the same value of quantum spin as a proton or an electron. They say that if it is a bound state of an electron and proton it should display the quantum spin of them both. To me it was pretty obvious that if a light electron is bound by a massive proton, it would be all but 'lost from view' so that its quantum spin would be hidden. The inertia of the proton, conferred by its greater mass, would account for the neutron appearing with the spin of the proton. For the physicists who contend that the law of Conservation of Angular Momentum does not allow for the spin of an electron to be lost, I would reply that physics does allow for conservation laws to be upheld in the formation and decay of unstable particles; so long as nothing is gained or lost in the overall process. Electron spin would be conserved in the overall process of formation and decay of the neutron because an electron going in would have the same spin as an electron coming out.

It seemed to me that physicists were clinging to straws in their arguments against the obvious structure of the neutron. It appeared they were attempting to cover something up. There had to be a really good reason why they were so determined that a neutron is not an electron locked on a proton. I was working on *The Vortex : Key to Future Science* with Peter Hewitt when he uncovered the clue. It turned out that the bound state theory for the neutron threatened the foundations of quantum theory; the most sacred cow of science...

The major pillar of quantum theory is the system of quantum mechanics based on a *principle of indeterminacy* proposed, in 1927, by the German physicist Werner Heisenberg. He suggested that the process of making certain measurements in the sub-atomic world would increase the uncertainty about what was going on there. For example, if you wanted to look at a particle in order to ascertain its position, you would have to reflect light off it. But, the act of bouncing light off the particle would give it a kick that would increase its momentum and so make its position more uncertain. Looking at small objects requires more energy than is required for looking at large ones. This is evident in the electron-microscope which employs higher frequency radiation than a light microscope. Because sub-atomic particles are the smallest things in nature, the action of ascertaining their position with any degree of certainty would require a very great energy which would give them an enormous kick. Heisenberg argued against being able to determine, with any certainty, both the position and the momentum of a particle. He formulated his law as a simple mathematical indeterminacy between time and energy and the momentum and position of a particle, which came to be known as the *uncertainty principle*.

The neutron, discovered five years after the uncertainty principle was proposed, offered an ideal experimental test for the principle. If a neutron is treated as an electron bound to a proton, the position and momentum of the electron could be defined with a high degree of certainty. The position of the electron would be somewhere within a space defined by the estimated size of the neutron and its momentum could be ascertained from the energy locked up in the mass of the neutron that exceeds the sum mass of an electron and proton.

The rest mass of an electron is $0.911 \times 10^{-30}$ kg. The rest mass of a proton is $1672.62 \times 10^{-30}$ kg. The rest mass of a neutron is $1674.92 \times 10^{-30}$ kg, therefore, it has a mass of $1.389 \times 10^{-30}$ kg in excess of the sum mass of an electron and proton. This is equal to 1.5 x the rest mass of an electron. In the neutron, an electron could not possess a momentum in excess of that allowed by the energy locked up in this mass.

If Heisenberg's principle is applied to an electron confined in the space of a neutron, the high degree of certainty in its position demands of it an enormous indeterminacy in momentum. The uncertainty principle predicts that electrons bound in a neutron could have momentum values requiring velocities as high as 99.97% of the velocity of light. To reach that order of velocity, the electron would have to possess energy up to the equivalent of approximately 40 x its rest mass. If the Heisenberg principle were valid, then neutrons - as bound states of electrons and protons - would occur with a wide range of masses reflecting the indeterminacy of the momentum of their constituent electrons. Neutron mass values would be expected to range from $1673.5 \times 10^{-30}$ kg to $1710 \times 10^{-30}$ kg reflecting electrons with zero momentum and electrons with velocities approaching the velocity of light. In fact neutrons possess the very precise mass of $1674.92 \times 10^{-30}$ kg. This indicates that there is no detectable indeterminacy in the momentum of their constituent electrons.

One way to save the uncertainty principle is to say it does not apply to neutrons. Electron-proton couples, in which electrons orbit protons, are already excluded from the principle. Particles moving in orbits, under the inverse square law of attraction, are excluded from the uncertainty principle because the *line spectra* of atoms produced by changes of electron orbits are exact. Some physicists may be tempted to treat the neutron as a proton with an electron in a very tight high energy orbit so that it can also be excluded from the uncertainty principle. However, Wu's discovery and the electric dipole moment of the neutron, indicate that the electron is bound on a specific site in the neutron. This means it cannot be excluded under the orbital laws as a valid test for the uncertainty principle and if physics makes too many exclusions to protect the uncertainty principle, then it could be accused of rejecting experiments which challenge the validity of its theories; and according to Richard Feynman, *if your theories and mathematics do not match up to the experiments then they are wrong.*

The Heisenberg uncertainty principle was never an easy law to test experimentally, because that required a certain measure of the simultaneous position and momentum of a sub-atomic particle which the principle stated was virtually impossible to obtain with certainty. Treating the neutron as a bound state of electron and proton offered physicists a rare opportunity for testing the uncertainty formula, and the fact that it clearly fails suggests that Heisenberg's principle is wrong.

Many people will protest that Heisenberg' principle must be right because of its incredible success in the *New Physics*. However, the successful application of a principle does not prove its validity. Just as a car can run without passing a roadworthy test so a theoretical principle can work even if it is fundamentally wrong. With the failure of the uncertainty principle and the quark theory it could be said that the New Physics is running without a certificate of roadworthiness. Maybe the time has come for it to be scrapped!

Scientists might argue that the 1957 measure of the electric dipole moment was too inaccurate to be taken as a serious threat to their most important theory. I would reply that there have been technological advances since 1957. If scientists were really interested, this measure would have been repeated with more advanced equipment so that a more accurate result could be obtained. Why, in nearly 40 years, has this not occurred?

To me it is patently obvious that rather than admit that the uncertainty principle is unsound, physicists have done their best to dismiss the experimental data about the neutron. Like the mad professor in my story, they vehemently deny that the neutron is an electron-proton plum pudding and insist that it is a quark gâteau instead! It is hard to see how they could do otherwise because, if Heisenberg's principle was shown to be invalid, then the entire edifice of quantum mechanics would collapse like the proverbial house built upon sand, and to the modern physicist that is unthinkable. In the words of professor A.J. Leggett, "...quantum mechanics...has had a success which is almost impossible to exaggerate. It is the basis of just about everything we claim to understand in atomic and sub-atomic physics, most things in condensed-matter physics, and to an increasing extent much of cosmology. For the majority of practising physicists today it is the correct description of nature, and they find it difficult to conceive that any current or future problem of physics will be solved in other than quantum mechanical terms. Yet despite all the successes, there is a persistent and, to their colleagues, sometimes irritating minority who feel that as a complete theory of the Universe, quantum mechanics has feet of clay, indeed 'carries within it the seeds of its own destruction'."

Quantum mechanics came to depend upon the uncertainty principle after Enrico Fermi had the idea that forces could be carried between particles by the exchange of other particles. In 1934, a young Japanese physicist, Hideki Yukawa, picked up Fermi's idea and developed it successfully through the uncertainty principle. He suggested that, within the bounds of sub-atomic uncertainty, particles could borrow energy from the Universe to bring about the creation of short-lived force-carrying particles. So long as the force-carrying particles were sufficiently unstable to decay and repay the energy debt within the time allotted by Heisenberg's formula then no conservation law would have been broken in the overall process of their formation and demise. If the time span of their existence was short enough, the uncertainty principle allowed for very large amounts of energy to be involved in the formation of the particles which would, in turn, enable them to carry very powerful forces. Yukawa used this to predict the existence of *meson* particles to carry the strong nuclear force.

Yukawa's underlying premise appeared to be that 'anything is possible behind the screen of uncertainty'. His idea, that sub-atomic particles run credit with the Universe, as though it were a bank, is completely crazy but because it is impossible to be certain that it doesn't happen, no one could argue with Yukawa when he claimed that it does happen. Yukawa used uncertainty in the microcosm to argue his thesis, much as medieval philosophers used uncertainty in the macrocosm to argue how many angels could stand on a pinhead.

Yukawa's idea would seem to confirm a statement in the Talmud which says: *We see the world, not the way it is, but the way we are.* This law of projection would appear to apply in the way that 20th-century man perceives the 'quantum world'. With his mortgage, bank loan, and innumerable credit cards, the professional physicist runs his affairs on credit, like most other people in the modern world. It is this image that physicists have projected onto the sub-atomic world. The proton is imagined to undergo energy borrowing in order to create gluons for the binding of quarks, W and Z particles for the weak nuclear force, mesons for the strong nuclear force, *virtual-photons* for the forces of electric charge and magnetism and *gravitons* for the force of gravity. Whilst attempts have been made to unify the theory, so that the proton makes only one borrowing from universal energy

- the one, grand unified GUT account - the projected image of credit accounts is undeniable.

There is a more serious reason why physicists have accepted the energy credit system of quantum mechanics so universally. The theory has been spectacularly successful in predicting the outcome of experiments. This happened when Yukawa's mesons were discovered, quite dramatically in 1947, in the *cosmic ray* research of Professor Cecil Powell. Yukawa's idea was accepted because of the scientific method which allows a theory to be treated as proven if it can successfully predict the outcome of an experiment. Karl Popper made it clear that the scientific method should be used only to disprove theories but scientists have attempted to use it as a criterion to prove their theories. It would be naive to imagine that theorists would make predictions in order that their theories can be disproved and themselves discredited. It is human nature to aim for success, not failure. In the real world, theorists live in hope that experiments will uphold their predictions and pave the way for a Nobel prize - as proved to be the case for Yukawa.

Whilst it cannot be denied that many theoretical predictions have led to major discoveries in physics - such as Yukawa's which led to the discovery of mesons - there is great danger in putting too much store by predictions. The spectacular vindication of a prediction can cause a sensation which is liable to give more credence to a theory than it is worth. Why should a theory be treated as true if it makes a successful prediction? There can be a number of different explanations for a scientific experiment or observation. For example, it cannot be denied that mesons exist, but just because Yukawa predicted them does not mean that his explanation for them is correct. It could be a coincidence that he managed to predict their mass and lifespan from his thesis. A completely different explanation for mesons could follow Yukawa's. It might work as well and not demand that primary particles have arbitrary, anthropomorphic properties. However, appearing as an explanation for mesons rather than a prediction, it could pass unnoticed, because predictions drive the machinery of science. They suggest directions for research and designs for experiments. Scientific experiments are generally designed by the researchers to look for things that have been predicted by the theorists. Experiments are also biased by the scientists who design and interpret them according to whether they want to prove or disprove something.

Many people demand proof for truth. They believe that something must be true if it is proven by a scientific experiment or false if it doesn't lend itself to the scientific method. This attitude is naive because the philosophy of science does not allow for the existence of absolute truths. Predictions can only establish the use, never the truth of a theory. The scientific method can only establish which theories are most useful to science; and these theories could be myths.

I honestly believe that the 'prediction rule' in the scientific method is a serious weakness. Crazy theories have become accepted in physics because they have fulfiled the prediction criteria of the scientific method. This is why Niels Bohr could jest, at the end of a lecture given by Wolfgang Pauli in 1958, "We are all agreed that your theory is crazy. The question which divides us is whether it is crazy enough."

This weakness in the scientific method shows itself in quantum mechanics where predictions, incorporating the uncertainty principle, have been gloriously vindicated by experiment. For example, Feynman's theory of virtual photons is contained in a branch of quantum theory called *Quantum Electro Dynamics (QED)*. QED is the most successful theory in the history of science with a margin of error in the order of only one part in three billion. A failure of the uncertainty principle could collapse the quantum theory for electro-magnetic forces which would throw the validity of the scientific method into question and undermine the very foundations of science. It could then be argued that  scientists are simply proving what they believe. I happen to believe that we create our own reality. It is no surprise to me that experiments reflect the beliefs of the people performing them.

The theories of quantum mechanics cannot stand if the Heisenberg uncertainty principle is invalidated by the neutron. If the neutron is a bound state of electron and proton then the outstanding experimental success of quantum mechanics will have done little more than reveal just how effective science can be in establishing myths. It is hardly surprising that when the neutron appeared, as a black swan, over the quaint little pond of quantum mechanics, instead of welcoming its arrival - as scientific integrity would demand - physicists tried to shoot it. Had they allowed it to land, Heisenberg's principle would have been a dead duck and the virtual force-carrying particles, their darling little ducklings, would have certainly drowned. Failing to submerge it, they muddied the waters with incomprehensible maths, whitewashed it with quark and with a flap about quantum spin, chased it away.

In the pre-scientific era, theories were built up by heaping speculation upon speculation. Medieval theologians were speculating that if an angel were chopped in half, two angels would emerge because new halves would grow on the split ends. Philosophers were adding epicycles to Ptolemy's complex description of the solar system to accommodate new discoveries in astronomy whilst alchemists were involved in an endless desperate search for the philosopher's stone. History would appear to be repeating itself in physics as speculation is heaped upon speculation and the endless search for hypothetical particles becomes ever more desperate. Meanwhile, protons, neutrons and electrons, the real stuff of matter, remain unexplained. It is the story of the *Emperor's New Clothes* all over again. Quarks and the virtual particles of quantum mechanics are phantoms that don't exist, but few people in physics care to admit to this because there are too many jobs, academic reputations and Nobel prizes at stake. However, there is no future for science if awkward facts are swept under the carpet to save the theories. In the words of George Gamow, "Staggering contradictions of this kind, between theoretical expectations on the one side and observational facts or even common sense on the other, are the main factors in the development of science."

In his Inaugural Lecture, Stephen Hawking said that because of the Heisenberg uncertainty principle, the electron could not be at rest in the nucleus of an atom. The fact is that electrons are bound within atomic nuclei and it is precisely because of this undeniable evidence that 'the end is in sight for theoretical physics'. The awkward facts about the proton and neutron could mean the end of theoretical physics as we know it. However, this may not be a bad thing. Appearing as pillars of truth and harbingers of change, the evidence of these natural particles will enable us to sweep the myths out of modern physics and clear the way for a new approach to quantum theory and a completely new understanding of the Universe.

Chapter 2

# THE QUANTUM BANDWAGON

*"Quantum theory...you never understand it, you just get used to it."*

*Richard Feynman*

Unlike the theories of relativity, the quantum theory is not based on a single idea developed by a lone genius. It grew up in the early part of the 20th century from a number of ideas contributed by several pioneering physicists, including Max Planck, Max Born and Werner Heisenberg from Germany, Erwin Schrödinger from Austria, Niels Bohr from Denmark, Count Louis de Broglie from France and Albert Einstein from Switzerland.

The quantum theory began in 1900 when Planck suggested that energy was radiated in discrete packets with wave properties. These packets he called *quanta*. In 1905, Einstein explained the results of an experiment called the *photo-electric effect* by showing that light consists of particles - quantum packets of energy - which came to be called *photons*. In a stroke, he put Planck's quantum hypothesis on the map and created a major dilemma in physics - was light a wave or a particle?

The wave properties of light had been well established, a century before, by Thomas Young, in contradiction to Newton's earlier particle theory for light. It was Einstein who established the wave-particle duality for light. Then in 1922, Louis de Broglie reversed this idea by suggesting that particles of matter could be treated as waves. His idea appeared to be confirmed in 1927, when two American scientists, Davisson and Germer, discovered that a beam of electrons created the same characteristic wave patterns as a beam of light. Wave-particle duality was thus extended to cover matter. Erwin Schrödinger embraced de Broglie's concept of particles moving in waves and in 1926, he developed a wave equation which could be applied to the motion of the electron in a hydrogen atom.

In 1897, Sir J.J. Thomson had discovered negatively charged electrons in the atom. Thomson imagined that electrons were stuck in the atom like plums in a pudding. Then, in 1911, Ernest Rutherford discovered, through radioactivity, that the atom was mainly space with a small dense nucleus. Rutherford suggested that the electrons orbited the nucleus much as planets do the sun. However, his simple model for the atom posed a problem. According to the known laws of physics, the orbiting electron should lose energy and spiral into the nucleus. In 1913 Bohr overcame this problem by suggesting that electrons occur in the atom with certain, clearly defined energies. Each level of energy would establish for it a stable orbit around the nucleus. He argued that the electron could only gain or lose energy in discrete quantum packets, which would shift it from one orbit to another. It could not, therefore, gradually lose energy and spiral into the nucleus. As Bohr applied the quantum principles of light to the atom and Schrödinger successfully applied his wave equation to the electron orbits, the clear distinction between matter and light began to dissolve.

Schrödinger also showed that the electron orbit could not be treated as certain. The position of the electron in the atom could only be deduced in terms of where it would most probably be according to its energy. In 1927, Heisenberg joined the team and introduced uncertainty into quantum theory, to stand alongside Schrödinger's probability. However, the introduction of probability and uncertainty into quantum theory was deeply distasteful to Einstein. He dismissed probability with the comment "God doesn't play dice," and he described the uncertainty principle as "...a real witches' calculus...most ingenious, and adequately protected by its great complexity against being proved wrong..."

He is known to have reduced the young Heisenberg to tears in his arguments and he continually clashed with Bohr, but Bohr was the powerful personality who won through in the end. He dominated the quantum theory in its early days and established the 'quantum bandwagon'. In the words of Robert Matthews, "At the reins of the quantum bandwagon were one or two superstars - like Niels Bohr - and in the back were like-minded theorists and experimentalists armed to the teeth with laboratory results to prove their case. If you get in the way of such a bandwagon, you will at best be left behind, and at worst be flattened."

According to Matthews, David Bohm drew attention to the dire consequences of this effect when he said, "Most physicists said they followed Bohr without really knowing what Bohr was doing."

Physicists were well aware that if their thinking did not conform to what was fashionable in physics they were liable to be swept aside by the current theoretical stream of thinking. Much of the success of quantum theory has been a result of this bandwagon effect.

Einstein was the true father of quantum physics but ignoring his intuition, Bohr pushed him off the wagon and into the ditch, and with Heisenberg at his side, drove it down an uncertain road. In the quark account for particles and quantum mechanical account for forces, the bandwagon picked up a couple of lame horses, then knocking over the 'neutron warning' sign and lurching from one ludicrous idea to another, it went hurtling on toward a dead end, carrying the whole of physics with it.

Physicists put more store by Heisenberg and Bohr than Einstein. In *A Brief History of Time*, Stephen Hawking wrote: "The main difficulty in finding a theory that unifies gravity with the other forces is that general relativity is a classical theory; that is it does not incorporate the uncertainty principle of quantum mechanics."

The fact that Einstein and his theories have been lumped in with the old classical physics is supported by Robert Matthews. He explained that "...Einstein...A classical physicist in the mould of Newton...could never accept that there are limits to knowledge, that the world is, at root, essentially and ineluctably unknowable. Having started the quantum revolution and led it for many years, he now became its most redoubtable critic..."

Uncertainty is now central to quantum theory and the new progressive physics, so uncertainty about the principle of uncertainty threatens the credibility of physics. This is unfortunate as modern physics represents one of the greatest achievements in history. I see the uncertainty principle as the rotten apple that is spoiling the barrel. I believe the time has come to abandon the Heisenberg/Bohr view of quantum reality and rebuild the quantum theory on the foundations established by Einstein. The distinction between classical and modern physics should have been drawn around the work of Einstein rather than Heisenberg and Bohr. Einstein was, after all, the leader of the revolution which upturned classical physics and the brightest star in the original quantum firmament. Certainly I think it was a grave error on the part of Bohr and his team to draw a distinction between classical and quantum physics on the issue of *realism*.

Up until the turn of the 20th century, there was a tendency to believe there was an ultimate reality that man, through experiment, could discover. Scientists believed that they could explain, in their theories, what these realities were. This way of thinking came to be known as the philosophy of realism. As scientists had to adopt different and incompatible wave and particle models to explain the same phenomenon, the inadequacy of theoretical models became apparent. This led to the *Copenhagen interpretation* of quantum theory which rejected realism as naive and denied that it was possible to construct theoretical models that were true representations of reality. However, physicists have found it hard to maintain a consistent posture. Like most people, they have tended to think of elementary particles as 'tiny little things' with definite properties such as mass, spin and electric charge. They could make beams of them and bounce them off each other, just like billiard balls. The truth is that whilst physicists contend that naive realism is a thing of the past, they still appear to have a deep conviction that their hypothetical particles are not just models but that they really exist. For example, with their particle accelerators, physicists hunt for hard, massy quarks at the core of matter because they believe that quarks are real.

Quantum physics was established by Planck and Einstein on the principle that everything is formed out of particles of energy, and I suggest that the distinction between classical and quantum physics be hinged on an understanding of energy, not realism. Planck broke ranks with classical physics by showing that radiant energy is particulate. Einstein then established a clear basis for the new physics by showing that matter and light could be described as particles of energy rather than particles of some material substance. Before Einstein, classical physics was rooted in materialism and Einstein showed that materialism was a myth.

The idea that there is a material substance underlying everything is fundamental to Western thinking. Aristotle taught that everything was formed out of the four fluid mediums, earth, air, fire and water - a way of thinking which gave rise to alchemy. Democritus taught that, "nothing exists except atoms and empty space; everything else is opinion", and his concept - that everything was formed out of atoms moving in empty space - is fundamental to modern scientific thinking. He picked up the atomic idea, around 500 B.C., from Leucippus who first conceived of ultimate particles, existing in matter, with predetermined properties. Democritus called them atoms and the concept was brought into the modern era by the writings of Epicurus (342-270 B.C.) and the Roman Lucretius (99-55 B.C.) in his poem *De Rerum*

*Natura.* Newton was inspired by Lucretius when he wrote in the *Opticks*: "It seems probable to me that God, in the beginning, formed matter in solid, massy, hard, impenetrable, moveable particles."

This thinking gave rise to the classical model of the billiard-ball atom, as the ultimate particle of matter with irreducible properties. Quarks are very reminiscent of billiard-ball atoms, as they are conceived to be the ultimate particles in matter, possessing irreducible properties such as mass and fractional charge, charm and strangeness. If Newton were alive today, perhaps he would have said: "It seems probable to me that in the big bang, matter formed mainly as massy, hard, up and down, top and bottom, strange, and charmed quarks."

I am not the only person to link quarks with the atomic hypothesis. Jim Dawson, writing in the the Minneapolis *Star Tribune* on May 15, 1994, opened his report on the supposed discovery of the top-quark at Fermilab in April 1994 with the statement: "So there we have it, after more than two thousand years of searching, all of the fundamental stuff of Democritus' atom has been revealed. The crowning moment came a couple of weeks ago, when physicists announced that a gigantic, 5,000-ton machine apparently had detected a very small particle called the top-quark." (In fact the physicists blasting away at Fermilab in Illinois, didn't actually see a top-quark. All they saw was debris - a jet of electrons and muons which they supposed to be the decay products of W-particles which, in turn, they assumed to be the breakdown products of a top-quark.)

Just as the classical atomic idea - fundamental to materialism - has persisted in modern physics, in the form of the quark theory, so Newton's corpuscular model for particles of light has also persisted in the minds of most physicists. Most physicists treat light as a stream of particles following a wave probability pattern. This idea embodies the classical atomic hypothesis - that everything is formed out of little particles in motion; in this case, wave motion.

Because it is fundamental to the programme of indoctrination in school science, physicists find the atomic hypothesis hard to relinquish; especially when it has been the most useful and successful idea in the history of science. As Richard Feynman said in *The Feynman Lectures on Physics*: "If, in some cataclysm, all of scientific knowledge were to be destroyed, and only one sentence passed on to the next generation of creatures, what statement would contain the most information in the fewest words? I believe it is the atomic hypothesis...that all things are made of atoms - little particles that move around in perpetual motion."

I contend that quantum mechanics is a classical theory. It is a recast of the atomic hypothesis, because it assumes the existence of particles that move. Gary Zukav exposed this assumption when he said that "...'quantum mechanics' is the study of the motion of quantities."

I believe quantum mechanics should be the study of quantities of motion. Energy is divided into particles but energy is the ability to do work which means it is, quite simply, activity or potential activity. A quantum of energy is more a particle *of* motion than a particle *in* motion. The most useful sentence to survive a cataclysm should summarise this new quantum hypothesis rather than the old atomic hypothesis. The new quantum hypothesis, concerned with the idea that everything is formed out of particles of energy, could be summarised in the sentence: *All things are made of energy - little particles of perpetual motion.* The difference between talking about particles that move and particles of movement may sound slight but it is all important. The understanding of the Universe hangs upon it.

On one hand, scientists proclaim that classical physics is a thing of the past, whilst on the other hand, they have turned the quantum concept into a classical theory. They have done this by assuming the existence of particles that move to account for everything at a fundamental level and the uncertainty principle has served to shroud these particles so that nobody can be really certain what they are.

The atomic hypothesis is the basis of scientific materialism. Even though physicists contend that scientific materialism is dead, most people still cling, with tenacity, to the naive realism promulgated by Democritus, that particles and space must first exist in order for there to be movement in the Universe. Most have failed to realise that a neo-classic materialism has survived in modern quantum mechanics. My definition of a scientific materialist is one who assumes the existence of particles that move. He may say the particles are energy and not material substance, but whilst he assumes that these are particles that move rather than particles of motion, he is projecting the atomic hypothesis which is the basis of classical, scientific materialism and the naive realism embodied in the model of the billiard-ball atom.

It is my belief that the divide between classical and quantum physics should not be over the issue of realism, it should be over the issue of materialism. The issue of realism is a red herring. The atomic hypothesis is a classical theory so if quantum mechanics assumes the existence of particles that move, it has to be classical. The true break with classical thinking came with Einstein in his challenge to materialism, not with Heisenberg and Bohr in their challenge to realism. Einstein was the real quantum theorist, driven out of quantum physics by classical thinkers masquerading as quantum physicists.

Einstein believed in movement. He believed that matter and light were related to movement rather than material substance. This was evident because, according to Einstein, the sole universal constant was the speed of light and though he never spoke about anything moving at the speed of light he held that everything in the known Universe was relative to this supreme speed of movement. At the same time he showed that matter could be equated with energy. By relating matter to energy and also to the speed of light he showed that energy must be movement at the speed of light. Einstein stood apart from the rest of science; he accepted the existence of movement but not the idea that there had to be something that moved. Einstein understood the real, non-material nature of the world in which we live. Few people really understood him and this, according to William Berkson, was "...not because of his ideas or the mathematics he employed, but because of his world view. Einstein denied the substantiality of matter and the field, whilst maintaining their reality."

Einstein stood alone as a non-classical theorist because he was able to take the tremendous leap of free thinking which allowed that movement could exist as the prime reality underlying particles of light and matter and also the space in which they move. He saw mass, space and time as being "...relative to the invariable speed of light".

The modern, materialistic mind cannot accept that everything is formed out of pure activity without any underlying substance; that nothing substantial really exists. When confronted by this stark reality in the definition of energy, the top physicists reply that they don't know what energy is. Richard Feynman made this clear in *The Feynman Lectures on Physics* when he said, "It is important to realise that in physics today, we have no knowledge of what energy is."

The problem is that the understanding of energy lies in the realm of metaphysics rather than physics and that is a no-go area for most establishment figures in science. Even the use of language presents a problem. Because the material philosophy predates modern language, words like movement, energy and activity have come to be understood as properties of things - first something exists then it moves or possesses energy! However, language must adapt to allow for new breakthroughs in our understanding of the Universe. If physics shows that there is no substance underlying energy, in the language we have to allow that movement can exist where no substantial things - be they particles or fluids - exist to move. Particles of energy are particles of pure activity. In fact, the original definition of the word energy as 'the potential work or power within' gives a precise description.

A particle of pure activity is an abstract rather than a concrete reality. As acts of abstraction, particles of energy are more like thoughts than things. This suggests that the Universe is a mind. It should not be difficult for the human mind to accept the Universe as a mind but if it were generally accepted that the Universe is a mind and particles of energy are the equivalent of thoughts, people might begin to ask: "Whose mind is it? Who is thinking?" Some would reply that: "The Universe is the mind of God! It is the thought of God that creates the world in which we live." They may even argue that in studying the Universe, scientists have been studying the mind of God. This is a rational conclusion that can be drawn from the new quantum hypothesis.

There are many people who would be excited at this link between the new quantum hypothesis and God and would welcome the opportunity it offers science to present an alternative to religion. This is not inconsistent with the original aim of science which was to break the power of establishment religion and release humanity from the stranglehold of religious fear and superstition. It was never the intention of the fathers of science to dismiss God and dispense with the human spirit altogether. Science was not intended to dictate people's beliefs, as did the religions, but to return to people their personal power by enabling them to deduce universal truths for themselves.

However, I do not like to use the word 'God' because that particular word has come to be loaded with religious and anthropic connotations. I prefer to suggest that if the Universe is a mind, then consciousness and intelligence must be the ground of everything. I perceive consciousness as the prime reality. Assuming there must be a being called God that is conscious is no different to assuming there must be a particle called the atom that possesses energy. Consciousness is God just as energy is the particle. There is nothing substantial underlying consciousness or energy. In reply to Democritus I would say: **"Only consciousness and energy exist, everything else is opinion."**

Because of its abstract nature, the Universe could be described as a dream. If the Universe is a dream then consciousness would be the dreamer. If you prefer to imagine the Universe as an unfolding vision then consciousness would be the visionary. Consciousness could also be described as the creator because particles, as acts of conscious abstraction, would exist as the creation of consciousness.

In the new quantum hypothesis, particles of matter and light are viewed as acts of abstraction, but understanding how acts of abstraction can give rise to matter and light poses another problem altogether. Also, what is potential energy and how are power and activity stored within the particles of matter that make up our world? These are questions that need to be answered.

Abstract reality cannot be grasped, it can only be represented by symbols and pictures. The abstract is represented by symbols in mathematics and by pictures in art. The human mind requires images to grasp and for that purpose pictures and models are vital in the task of comprehending the Universe.

The quantum theory is almost totally dominated by mathematics. If it is mathematics which gives bite to a physical theory, then quantum theory is all teeth. Like the elusive grin of the Cheshire cat, it lacks the discernible face and body of visual imagery that the mind can readily grasp. Bohr stood almost alone in providing a conceptual picture in quantum theory. His model for the atom, though substantially modified, still survives, seventy years on. Such is the power of a visual model. The models of physics, as hypothetical constructs, serve us with varying degrees of success in relating to the physical world. Classical physicists believed in their models. They may have gone too far in taking their models to be representative of the reality underlying nature but quantum theory went to the opposite extreme of denying the value of realistic models altogether. This has left quantum theory sorely lacking in tangible images for its realities and people need something for the mind to grasp. As the physicist Heinz Pagels said: "Something inside us doesn't want to understand quantum reality. Intellectually we accept it because it is mathematically consistent and agrees brilliantly with experiment. And yet the mind is not able to rest."

Some sort of realistic image for what is going on in the Universe, is demanded by the mind. With the lack of imagery in quantum theory it has been only natural for physicists to cling to the particle realism conveyed by the atomic hypothesis. Realism is inevitable and the particle realism of modern physics is no less naive than the realism of the 19th century. Rather than continue to heap scorn on the achievements of 19th-century physics, we could dig into that veritable chest of treasures, and find some gems.

Chapter 3

# WAVES AND
# VORTICES

*"Will some unknown young scientist find a new way of looking at fundamental physics that clarifies the picture and makes today's questions obsolete?"*

*Murray Gell-Mann*

I believe it is possible to make an entirely new approach to quantum theory by embracing the best insights of 19th- and 20th-century physics. To begin with, realistic images of fundamental entities are essential if an understanding of the Universe is to be intelligible to everyone. The models and analogies employed could be treated more as teaching aids than literal representations of the quantum world by those who fear realism and absolutism. The realism of the 19th century could be balanced with the uncertainty of the 20th to allow for the construction of useful models which are not to be mistaken for absolute truths.

A towering genius of late 19th-century science was Lord Kelvin. Kelvin was the father of thermodynamics - the science of energy. Quantum theory, which is concerned with energy, originated from a problem in thermodynamics so it is appropriate to look for the clue to a new, consistent image of the quantum world in the insights of Lord Kelvin.

In Kelvin's day the atom was considered to be the ultimate

particle of matter, but whilst Kelvin believed in atoms, he had moved beyond the classical assumption that the smallest particles in matter occurred, like billiard balls, with a wide range of irreducible properties. The atomic hypothesis, embodied in the billiard-ball model, was repugnant to him. Lord Kelvin found this model to be completely unsatisfactory because it offered no explanation for the most fundamental properties of particles of matter. He felt that the popular, materialistic view of matter was superficial and naive and he dismissed the billiard-ball atom as a "monstrous assumption".

In Kelvin's day it was taken for granted that the Universe was pervaded by a frictionless ether which transmitted waves of light like the ocean transmits water-waves. Like most scientists, Kelvin believed that light consisted of wave motion in the ether. He added to the theory the idea that atoms were vortices in the ether. He suggested that the whole Universe could be reduced to two fundamental forms of motion: waves and vortices. This was not just a minor idea that might have been overlooked. It had developed into a major theory that dominated physics in the latter half of the 19th century and continued to be taught at Cambridge until 1910. James Clerk Maxwell, a major proponent for the vortex idea, wrote in the Encyclopaedia Britannica of 1875, "...the vortex ring of Helmholtz, imagined as the true form of the atom by Thomson (Lord Kelvin), satisfies more of the conditions than any atom hitherto imagined", and J.J. Thomson said that the vortex theory for the smallest particles of matter "...has 'a priori' very strong recommendations in its favour... the vortex theory for matter is of a much more fundamental character than the ordinary solid particle theory."

I believe that just as the vortex provided a fundamental understanding of matter in the late 19th century, at the end of the 20th century a vortex hypothesis could be employed to show how matter is formed out of energy and how energy can be stored, in potential form, in the particles and forces associated with matter.

In his special theory of relativity, Einstein proclaimed that mass was equivalent to energy and that mass, space and time were relative to the speed of light. Einstein visualised matter as frozen light. The vortex model, by illustrating particles of matter as 'spinning light', could show how it is that vast amounts of energy are contained in minute amounts of matter. Einstein searched for a unified field and the vortex could be the key. Kelvin believed that vortex motion created the properties characteristic of matter. In the vortex he endeavoured to reduce the properties of matter to a single, underlying and unifying principle. As such he was moving toward a unified field theory but his stroke of genius was to describe the underlying principle as a form of movement. It only required the suggestion that this was energy and that the speed of movement was the speed of light and the mystery of matter might have been solved. Kelvin was so close. He described light as a wave motion and matter as vortex motion in the same field. But he failed on three counts. Firstly he limited his vortex model to a vortex ring, depicted by a smoke ring when he could have allowed for other types of vortex motion. Then he thought the vortex particle was the atom and finally he imagined the field was the ether.

Toward the end of Kelvin's career there were many new breakthroughs in understanding the so-called atom, such as spectral lines, which his vortex model could not explain. It was still decades before the atom was to be split, so he didn't envisage sub-atomic vortices. Instead, he abandoned his model even though others continued to believe in it. Then, at the turn of the century, when the ether theory was dismissed, with it went most of the ether models, including Kelvin's vortex.

I believe that there is value in the vortex idea if it is applied to the smallest particles of matter as originally intended by Kelvin. It is the sub-atomic particles, rather than the atoms themselves, which I have treated as vortices. The vortex idea is a casualty of the error in science of applying the term atom to the wrong thing; to a conglomeration of fundamental particles rather than to the particles themselves.

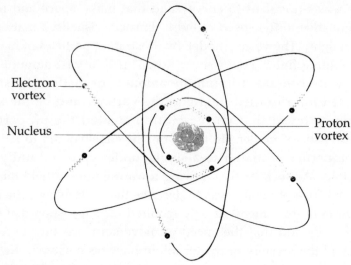

*Fig. 3.1 The new vortex atom*

However, I did not derive the idea that fundamental particles of matter could be vortices of energy from Kelvin. Kelvin's vortex atom is important to me only because it provides a historical precedent for the vortex idea in Western science. Furthermore, it is not considered necessary to provide a historical precedent or experimental justification for the axioms of a hypothesis  because as Einstein said, "The axiomatic basis of a scientific theory cannot be derived from experiment, it must be freely invented."

Nonetheless, I believe that the outmoded vortex atom from classical physics is closer to the truth than many of the arbitrary assumptions that have become fashionable in modern physics. Every generation has good and bad ideas but treats its own latest fashions in thought as more valuable than those that have gone before it. Crazy ideas come and go but worthwhile ideas survive the test of time. True ideas are persistent. If ever they are lost they crop up again in history. The vortex is just such an idea. The early atomists in ancient Greece, Democritus and Epicurus, believed that atoms formed bodies through vortex motion and thousands of years before them, mystics in ancient India considered vortex motion to be fundamental to matter. I discovered this in the *Advanced Course in Yogi Philosophy* by Yogi Ramacharaka, published around the turn of the 20th century, which reported that in the ancient Sanskrit records, energy - *prana* - was said to exist in matter - *akasa* - in the form of *vritta* - whirlpools or vortices.

Though many scientists and intellectuals scorn mysticism, through pure insight Indian mystics were able to anticipate Einstein in appreciating the most significant, scientific truth of our age, *that matter is a form of energy*. Perceiving the fundamental nature of matter as vortex energy, the mystics of ancient India provided me with a key to unlock many of the mysteries of modern physics. By treating sub-atomic particles as vortices of energy, I found a way of unifying relativity and quantum thinking and discovered the basis for a complete theory for the Universe which I have been able to communicate, in broad principle, to scientists and non-scientists alike. My work is more metaphysics than physics because the vortex led me to understand the first principles of nature but as I believe science should embrace both metaphysics and physics I make no apology for this. In fact the vortex has enabled me to forge a link between these two disciplines.

I developed my vortex science from the essence of Einstein's special theory of relativity and Planck's quantum theory. From those two great ideas I deduced that the activity which we call energy exists as the basis of everything. It is divided into particles and it occurs as movement at the speed of light. I did not assume the existence of anything that is moving, so, to my mind, quantum entities would not be objects so much as events at the speed of light.

Even though a quantum entity could never be grasped as a substantial thing it should be possible to represent it with a clear and simple model. The model I have chosen is a line of movement. The line would have no material substance. It would

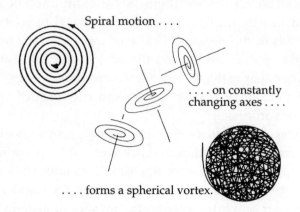

Spiral motion . . . .

. . . . on constantly
changing axes . . . .

. . . . forms a spherical vortex.

***Fig. 3.2*** *The spherical vortex of energy*

simply be a line of movement at the speed of light, represented by
the symbol *c*.

The movement of light exists with direction, therefore each
quantum entity would have to have a definite form based upon
the direction that the movement of light takes within it. There is
no evidence in nature for straight lines and there is certainly no
evidence that the fundamental particles of energy are based on
movements in straight lines. There is ample evidence in nature
for wave form, especially at a sub-atomic level. It would be
reasonable to suggest, therefore, that quantum entities occur in a
wave form and the model I use for this form of energy - which is
fundamental to light, heat, radio waves, gamma and X-rays - is a
line undulating in a bundle as a train of waves. The amount of
energy in the bundle, depicted by the length of the line, is
proportional to the number of waves it contains.

The energy in a quantum is represented by the formula $E=hf$
where $E$ quantifies energy, $h$ is Planck's constant and $f$ is
frequency. If the quantum is imagined as a bundle of folded line
then the length of line would be proportional to the number of
folds in the bundle. Thus, in the line model, energy would be

quantified as the length of line.

Physics has attempted to explain energy entirely in terms of its wave properties. I believe that in the wave physics has only 'half the story'. The vortex, as another fundamental form in nature, could be the basis of a fundamental form of energy. I believe this constitutes the other half of the story in quantum physics. If the line of movement, at the speed of light, were to spin on a single point, on constantly changing axes, it would create a *spherical vortex*. This is illustrated by a ball of wool.

If wool is wound on a single point, on constantly changing axes, it forms a ball. A ball of wool is the best model I have found to depict the spherical vortex forming a sub-atomic particle of matter. A ball of wool is static, but a quantum of spin at the speed of light would be dynamic and as such it would constitute a vortex. The spin of energy in the vortex is represented by the winding of the wool on or off the ball. Appearing as a ball, the spherical vortex defines a volume and corresponds closely to the accepted three-dimensional, corpuscular model for a sub-atomic particle of matter. (If $E$ quantifies energy and $c$ describes what energy is then a complete definition of energy would be $Ec$. If this is applied to Einstein's famous equation $E=mc^2$, then this becomes $Ec=mc^3$. In this expansion of the equation $m$, representing mass, quantifies matter and $c^3$ describes it as the movement of light distributed in three dimensions - assuming $c$ is a line - one dimension, $c^2$ is an area - two dimensions and $c^3$ is a volume - three dimensions. By defining energy in terms of activity at the speed of light, mass appears as a three dimensional form of this activity. The vortex, as a dynamic three dimensional spiral describes this form and so *mass* is defined as *quantity of vortex energy.)*

Two models are required for the sub-atomic vortex of energy. The vortex, as a three-dimensional spiral, suggests a continuous system of energy, whereas quantum theory suggests that energy is discontinuous. The vortex, as a discontinuous system of energy, could be depicted as a set of concentric spheres. The growth or decay of these concentric spheres of energy would depict the dynamic nature of the vortex. In fact, the sub-atomic vortex appears as a three-dimensional spiral, but acts as a system of concentric spheres. This is clear from my understanding of nuclear energy, where the vortex manifests as a three-dimensional spiral and from my understanding of electro-magnetism where it acts as a system of concentric spheres. One model defines its form and the other its behaviour.

There is no limit to the extension of concentric spheres of vortex energy. As the concentric spheres of energy expand, the intensity of energy in them may diminish but it would never fall to zero. The vortex energy can be stretched - and so diminish in its intensity - but it cannot vanish altogether because energy is neither created nor destroyed. I use the infinite extension of the vortex to account for the unlimited range of electric charge. I also use the infinite extension of the vortex to account for space. Close to its centre the vortex appears as a spiral space-path whereas, at a distance from its centre, the vortex appears as concentric spheres of space. This fits with the ball-of-wool model because a ball of wool tends to be more a three-dimensional spiral close to its centre and more a system of concentric spheres at a distance from the centre.

Because of its unlimited extension the concept of size cannot be applied to the vortex. One vortex particle can only be considered to be greater or lesser than another in terms of its *mass-energy*. The proton vortex contains 1836 times the energy contained in the mass of an electron. It is this mass-energy difference which is represented by the relative sizes of the vortices.

It is better to describe vortices in terms of inertia than in terms of size. The vortex hypothesis sheds considerable light on the subject of inertia when, like so many other things in physics, the fundamentals of inertia are little understood. As Richard Feynman said in the *Character of Physical Law*, "The law of inertia has no known origin".

Understanding that energy is nothing but pure motion, in the form of a vortex or a train of waves, explains inertia. Motion creates inertia. The concentric flow of vortex energy sets up a system of 'stay-put' or *static inertia* - the tendency of something to stay put unless it is forced to move. This would be a characteristic feature of the spherical vortex because the simultaneous flow of energy into or out of the vortex, in all directions, would tend to set up a resistance to movement of the vortex in any direction. It is this static inertia that we perceive as mass. Mass is created by the swirl of energy in the vortex and is a characteristic of this form of energy

Photons of light do not possess mass because they are based on wave, rather than vortex motion. Mass is a property of the vortex, not the energy within the vortex, therefore momentum laws, which incorporate mass and apply to vortices, cannot be applied to the energy within them. For example, the law of *Conservation of Angular Momentum* could not be applied to the energy forming the vortex.

The wave and vortex as fundamental forms of energy would give rise to the interactions and laws of physics and the Law of Conservation of Energy - largely attributed to Kelvin - suggests that these forms of motion are perpetual.

If the motion in the vortex and wave particles were not perpetual the Universe would have vanished a long while ago, so this fact is self-evident. (Individual electrons do disappear then reappear in the 'quantum leap' but as their sum total remains unaltered, collectively the electrons and protons that make up the physical world appear to be very stable.) The stability of the form of motion, in each particle of energy, is self-evident. If this were not so then the Universe would be completely amorphous. The stability of the vortex is also evident in the lifespan of electrons and protons, of which most of matter is composed. The proton, for instance, has an estimated lifespan of $10^{33}$ years. The durability of the wave form is also evident from the ability of photons to survive journeys through space lasting billions of years. A change in the form of a particle of energy would be expected to occur, not through its spontaneous decay but through its interactions with other particles.

Particles of energy, as perpetual acts of abstraction cannot be grasped as substantial things, they can only be detected through their interactions with one another. Physics is concerned with the interactions between particles of energy, and the interactions between the vortex and wave forms are most important because these are the basis of all useful structures and actions in our world. I have formulated two, very simple laws which embody the innate stability of the two fundamental forms of energy and govern their interactions. These I call: *The Quantum Laws of Motion.*

If everything is formed out of particles of perpetual motion then the most fundamental laws of the Universe would have to be laws of motion. Also, if particles of movement are inherently stable then stability should be a primary feature of these laws. Newton proposed laws of motion which govern our everyday lives. However, these should be a reflection of more fundamental laws of motion which operate in the world of the quantum, because everything is built on quantum reality. Newton stated, as his first law of motion, that, *"every body will continue in its state of rest or uniform motion in a straight line unless compelled by some external force to act otherwise."* Newton's laws are the laws of inertia. Systems of motion have an inertia to maintain their state of motion and it requires a force to change them. This principle is illustrated by children. It usually takes force to stop them doing what they are doing and get them to do something different and the order almost invariably meets with resistance. This is embodied in Newton's second law that, *"action meets with reaction".*

Newton based his laws on the behaviour of large bodies of matter, consequentially they have to be modified if they are to apply at a quantum level. For example, energy is not movement in a straight line. The particles of energy, described as quanta by Planck and photons by Einstein, possess wave motion, yet no external force has ever been observed to cause their motion to deviate from a straight into a wavy line. These quanta appear to maintain their state of wave-motion until they undergo an interaction with a particle of matter. This is a form of inertia which could be described as *wave-kinetic inertia*. By the same token a vortex particle of matter will maintain its relative state of rest unless another particle acts upon it to propel it into motion. This, I have already described as its static inertia, or mass.

I suggest, as a first Quantum Law of Motion that: *Particles of energy maintain their state or form of motion unless a change is forced upon them.* From the innate stability of vortex and wave, it follows that: *Once the force of change is removed then the particle of movement will revert to its original form.* This I propose as a second Quantum Law of Motion. The two Quantum Laws of Motion are illustrated by a coiled spring. The form of a spring is altered by the application of a force but on release of the force, it reverts to its original shape again.

In physics we are taught that motion results from the application of a force. This is putting the cart before the horse. All forces are derived from motion; the motion we call energy. Motion is the prime reality and the force it creates results from the form of the quantum of motion. A particle of energy, radiating in wave form will force a vortex into wave motion. A particle of energy in vortex form will force a wave train of energy to become transformed into mass.

If the vortex presents itself to a wave train of energy as a spiral space path, then radiant energy would follow the contours of space much as a car follows the bends in a road. Just as a car is forced to follow a curved path when it enters a roundabout on the road, so the wave-kinetic travelling energy, following the contour of spiral space, would move in toward the centre of the vortex. Close to the centre of the vortex the kinetic energy would be transformed into mass as it is forced into vortex motion. Travelling into an ever tighter spiral space-path, the wave train of energy would become trapped or *captured*. I postulate that vortices, such as the proton and neutron, are sufficiently massive to *completely capture* particles of travelling energy whereas light electron vortices can only *partially capture* a particle of travelling energy. I support this postulate by using it to explain wave-particle duality and mass-energy transformations; two major enigmas in physics today.

The electron vortex transforms the tip of the wave train into mass and by means of this transformation it captures the travelling particle of energy. The remaining wave-kinetic energy, which is not transformed into mass, could be imagined as sticking out of the vortex like a tail. It acts to force the vortex forward in wave motion. Through this interaction, the wave train and vortex become a composite of the two forms of energy. Each imposes its inertia onto the other. The wave train causes the electron to be a wave-particle as it moves and the vortex causes the captured energy to slightly increase its mass.

The wave-vortex couple could be imagined as a tadpole with the vortex as the head and the partially captured wave train of energy as the tail. Just as a tadpole swims in wave motion because it is propelled by the wave motion of its tail, because of the motion of its captured wave-kinetic energy, the vortex would move as a wave-particle. In the pond, a few tadpoles grow massive by devouring their lesser siblings. This image of the cannibal tadpole is useful in understanding the way particles grow more massive as they are accelerated in a particle accelerator.

As successive wave trains drive into a vortex it accelerates. (This occurs with protons and neutrons, after they are saturated with energy in complete capture. They can then take on more energy in partial capture which forces them into wave motion.) As part of each incoming wave-train is transformed into mass, proportionately more energy would be required to accelerate the vortex through each increasing increment of velocity. As the velocity of the vortex particle approaches the velocity of the accelerating wave-trains, the increase in its mass would progress

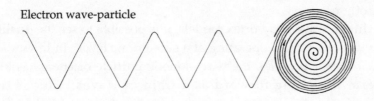

Electron wave-particle

***Fig. 3.3*** *Wave particle duality*

exponentially toward infinity. (The increase in mass of a particle, with acceleration, was predicted by Einstein in his special theory of relativity.)

Partial capture of wave energy, by a vortex, could also be depicted by the analogy of a monkey and a jar of nuts. The monkey would represent the wave train of travelling energy and the jar of nuts the vortex. The monkey can get its hand into the jar, but with a fistful of nuts it can't withdraw its hand, so it becomes partially captured by the jar. Rather than let go of the nuts the monkey races off taking the jar with it. The jar takes on the mobility of the monkey and is heavier because it contains the hand of the monkey.

Whilst the electron vortex may have a relatively low mass-energy, it could still present a tight spiral space-path at its centre so the first wave train of energy it captures would be tightly bound to it. The resultant bound state of wave and vortex would be very stable. According to the first Quantum Law of Motion, whilst this state persists, the electron would have mass slightly greater than its theoretical rest mass and it would also possess perpetual wave-kinetic energy. This would account for the ground-state of the electron in an atom, which is its most stable state. In its ground-state, such as in the hydrogen atom, an electron can orbit a proton indefinitely. The ground-state electron can be illustrated by the image of marriage. Just as in a marriage each partner imposes their personality on the other, so it is that each type of energy imposes its form of motion - its inertia - onto the other.

In the wave and vortex models, it is possible to see the duality of male and female operating at a sub-atomic level. In the *sex life of sub-atomic particles,* the wave-kinetic particle of energy is like sperm travelling forward as a train of waves. This is the masculine form of energy which underlies heat and light. The vortex particle of energy could be depicted as an ovum. It is spherical, static and receptive. This is the feminine form of energy which underlies matter. (In the native American tradition, light is seen as masculine and matter as feminine - which is why they speak of 'Grandfather Sun' and 'Grandmother Earth'.)

The sex life of sub-atomic particles provides an imaginative account for the concepts of work and entropy. Consider a man, roaming off into the unknown where he becomes lost and dissipated, leaving a woman behind at home, frustrated and fruitless. Left to itself, heat or light will radiate out into space and become dissipated. On their own, particles of matter will collapse into a black hole. Nothing useful happens when the masculine and feminine forms of energy are left to themselves. This is entropy. The opposite to entropy is work. Work describes the useful processes in physics resulting from the activation of matter by heat and light. The wave-vortex couple not only gives the vortex kinetic energy, which enables it to do work, it also enables the vortex to form useful structures - such as atoms. Wave-vortex coupling is illustrated by the young man who meets and marries a girl then he settles down to work.

When a sexual interaction occurs, the male takes the action of entering the female. She invites the interaction by being irresistibly attractive to him. This graphically illustrates the interaction between wave and vortex. The vortex takes no action in the coupling. It is irresistibly attractive to the wave train by presenting it with a spiral space-path. The wave train takes all the action in the coupling, as it drives itself into the vortex.

Now imagine the scene of a stable marriage disrupted by the

entry of a lover. The triangle is exciting but it doesn't last. The bond between husband and wife is strong so the lover leaves, and the marriage returns to monogamy again. This sort of thing goes on all the time in the sex life of sub-atomic particles. If an atom is bombarded with wave trains of energy in the form of heat or light, electrons will absorb some of the energy and leap into an excited state. (Protons, partaking in partial capture, could also exist in a similar excited state.)

The tight, central region of the electron vortex would already be occupied by the wave train responsible for its ground-state. This would be represented by the strong social bond between the man and his wife. Another packet of wave energy, coming in like a lover, is partially captured in more peripheral regions of the vortex, so the bond between the new energy and the electron vortex is not strong - this is why the excited state of an electron is far less stable than the ground state. This situation would be represented by the weak social bond between the wife and her lover. After a while, the loosely bonded wave-train of energy radiates away from the excited electron, leaving it to fall back into the ground state again, until a new wave-packet enters the scene. This is represented by the triangle breaking apart, the lover leaving and the marriage reverting back to its original monogamous state - until another lover arrives to create some more excitement.

The wave train of energy, radiating away like a disillusioned lover, appears as a photon of light. This process explains fire. Energy from the combustion of the fuel causes electrons, in the atoms rising in the hot air currents, to leap into an excited state. As they fall back to the ground state, photons of light are emitted. This accounts for the radiation of light from the flames. The boundary of the flame represents the minimum temperature, of the rising air, required for this process to occur. Electrons in atoms are very fussy about their lovers! Each quantum lover has to have what it takes - by way of a minimum amount of energy - to lift his electron mistress to a pre-determined level of excitement. In each atom, electrons can only occur in certain clearly defined energy states, therefore the electron can only absorb energy equivalent to the change in its energy state. On returning to its original state, the electron releases a packet of energy equivalent to the difference in the two energy states. The colour of a flame originates from this. As electrons, in the atoms dancing in the flames, fall back from the excited to the ground state, photons of light radiate away with a frequency equivalent to the energy difference between the excited and ground states.

Einstein established that the photon is a bundle of energy which exhibits the properties of both wave and particle. It could be depicted as a discrete, very localised wave-packet. In 1900, Planck had applied the equation $E=hf$ to the quantum which he described as a fundamental particle of energy. However, the term quantum is misleading because it applies to a photon and the photon is not a fundamental particle of energy. The photon is a bound state of two, more fundamental particles of energy. Maxwell's theory for light depicted it as two fields of energy, oscillating at right-angles. This model is supported by experiments in physics such as fluorescence and polarisation. In these experiments only one of the fields in the photon reacts with matter. This is also evident from photography. Only one field of energy in light reacts with the photographic plate. It would appear that the other field doesn't have any part to play in the

Two wave trains of energy
oscillating at right angles.

*Fig. 3.4* *The photon*

world of matter.

In 1932 the American physicist Carl Anderson, working at the California Institute of Technology, discovered there are sub-atomic particles that have no part to play in the normal world of matter. These particles of *anti-matter* had been predicted four years earlier by Paul Dirac, an English theorist working at Cambridge, and they seemed like science fiction until Anderson saw evidence of a positively charged electron - a *positron* - in a cosmic ray photograph.

Anderson found that he could produce electron-positron pairs of particles by bombarding lead with *gamma rays*. However, this only occurred if the energy in each photon exceeded the sum mass-energy of the two particles. This *threshold energy* showed that the two particles were generated from a single photon. Anderson's discovery established, beyond doubt, that the photon consists of two particles of energy, each of which can be transformed into an elementary particle of matter or anti-matter. It established that each photon must consist of a presumptive particle of matter and a presumptive particle of anti-matter. Because anti-matter does not exist in the normal world of matter, it makes sense that the presumptive anti-matter field in light would not react with matter. Experiments with anti-matter also lend support to the wave-train model for the photon.

Anderson confirmed that when a positron encountered an

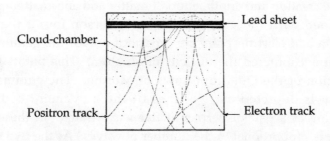

*Fig. 3.5* *Cloud chamber tracks of matter and anti-matter*

electron, they annihilated - as predicted by Dirac. The product of their annihilation was generally two photons which moved off in opposite directions. These annihilation photons were used in a fascinating experiment conducted at Berkeley in 1972, by John Clauser and Stuart Freedman. Clauser and Freedman arranged for the annihilation photons to pass through polarising filters and into photomultipliers to record them. When they inverted one photon, they found that the other one flipped over as well so that they were both plane polarised at the same time. A simple and obvious explanation for this result is forthcoming if the photon is treated as a long entity so that its 'tip' can enter the polarising filter before its 'tail' has left the site of its generation. As the tip of one photon is flipped, its tail would obviously invert with it. The tail of the first photon could then flip over the tail of the second photon, which would be leaving from the same point of generation in the opposite direction. This would be reflected immediately by the inversion of the tip of the second photon entering the opposite polarising filter. So the *Clauser and Freedman experiment* lends considerable support to the idea that the particle of light is a train of waves, rather than a point-like entity. (Photons would appear as points, even if they were long entities because they travel at very nearly the speed of light. According to the theory of relativity, as speeds approach that of light, distances appear to shrink so that a photon travelling at the speed of light could be infinitely long but still appear to be a point.)

The creation and annihilation of matter and anti-matter can be explained with the vortex model. Anderson found that the positron and electron pairs are produced only if the gamma ray photon encountered the nucleus of an atom. This points to an operation of the Quantum Laws of Motion. The gamma ray photon is depicted as two lines of the movement of light, occurring as a pair of perpendicular wave trains. In these, the energy is proportional to the number of waves. As the two wave trains enter the intense vortex energy extending out from the nucleus of an atom, the first Quantum Law of Motion would come into operation and each one would be transformed into a vortex of energy. The two new vortices appearing on the other side of the nucleus, as an electron-positron pair, would have a sum mass and kinetic energy equivalent to the energy of the gamma ray photon.

As the positron loses its kinetic energy, it is drawn toward an electron by opposite charge. The attraction between the two particles culminates in their mutual annihilation. This annihilation of matter and anti-matter can be understood in terms of two vortices of equal size, but opposite direction of spin, coming together. As they do so, the two opposite directions of vortex motion cancel each other out. Being of equal mass, the mutual annihilation of vortex motion goes to the heart of each particle. The second Quantum Law of Motion then comes into operation as the two lines of the movement of light revert to their original wave form and radiate away. The interesting feature of this operation of the second law, is that a new electron comes into existence as an old one disappears. At the end of the process, however, the energy accounts are settled as, between them, the two annihilation photons carry away the energy of the original

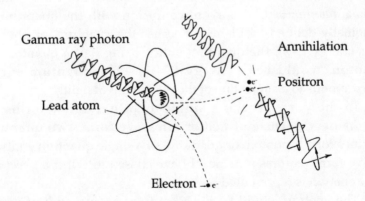

*Fig. 3.6 The creation and annihilation of matter and anti-matter*

If the basic particle propulsion unit is half a photon . ...

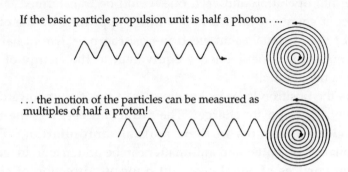

... the motion of the particles can be measured as
multiples of half a proton!

**Fig. 3.7** *Quantum mechanics*

gamma ray photon (apart from the kinetic energy of the pair lost
prior to annihilation), so energy is conserved. The creation and
annihilation of matter and anti-matter also support the link
between vortex energy and the electric charge of sub-atomic
particles, because Lord Rutherford and Frederick Soddy
described the creation and annihilation of matter and anti-matter
in terms of a Law of Conservation of Electric Charge.

The formation of an elementary particle from half a photon
confirms that half the photon, or quantum of energy, is more
fundamental than the whole photon or quantum. I have called
this a *quantum entity* to avoid confusion with the quantum as
originally defined by Planck. Because the quantum, or photon,
has energy $E=hf$, the quantum entity, being half a quantum or
photon, would have energy $E=\frac{1}{2}hf$. The quantum entity
corresponds to a single line of the movement of light.

In the vortex form, a single quantum entity forms an
elementary particle of matter. In wave form, two quantum
entities form a photon, or quantum, so a single quantum entity in
wave form requires a name. I have chosen to call it an *enetron*.
The enetron is represented by $\frac{1}{2}h$.

The enetron would be the most fundamental unit of wave-
kinetic energy. Vortices could only acquire energy, in complete or
partial capture, as complete enetrons therefore they will gain or

lose kinetic energy in multiples of enetrons. In quantum mechanics the kinetic energy of elementary particles occurs as integer multiples of $\frac{1}{2}h$. If the denomination of the Universal penny happens to be $\frac{1}{2}h$, it makes sense that quantum interactions can be accounted in integer multiples of half Planck's constant.

To understand this point imagine energy as money. Financial transactions, involving millions of pounds, can be accounted for as multiples of pennies. In the world at large, mechanical events involve quantities of energy comparable to multi-billion pound transactions. Quantum mechanics, is concerned with the kinetics of elementary particles, which involves quantities of energy comparable to pennies. If the universal penny happens to be an enetron, it makes sense that quantum interactions can be accounted in multiples of enetrons. (Quantum mechanics incorporates a property of particles called *quantum spin*. Because quantum spin is denoted by $\frac{1}{2}h$, it could be that when a particle is said to have quantum spin denoted by $\frac{1}{2}h$, this means it is formed out of a single quantum entity - a single line of the movement of light.)

Chapter 4

# NUCLEAR
# ENERGY

*"Nuclear energy...we have the formulas for that, but we do not have the fundamental laws. We know that it is not electrical, not gravitational and not purely chemical, but we do not know what it is."*

*Richard Feynman*

There are many manifestations of energy. Imagine picking up a piece of flint from the beach. *Potential energy* describes the energy stored by the flint. For example, whilst it is in your hand the flint stores energy that would be released should it fall and strike the ground. The potential energy is transformed into *kinetic energy* if you let the flint fall. The flint falls because of *gravitational energy*. As it strikes the shingle, *radiant energy* can be seen in a spark and *sound energy* is heard. The flint gains *heat energy* in the warmth of your hand. *Chemical energy* was involved in forming the flint millions of years ago and it is *electrical energy* which holds the flint in crystalline form through the continual interaction of electrons and protons in its atoms. At the same time, however, the very substance of the flint itself can be reduced to energy. Physicists refer to *mass-energy* when they talk about energy trapped in sub-atomic particles or atomic nuclei and *nuclear energy* when this trapped energy is released.

In classical physics, energy was defined as *the ability to do work.* It was understood as the ability of things to act and move. In modern physics this simplistic understanding of energy became confused by the discovery that nuclear energy could be derived from the destruction of mass. The classical definition of energy appeared to have collapsed. However, with the vortex, it is possible to picture mass as a form of energy. When, in an atomic explosion, mass is destroyed to give rise to violent activity, this release of nuclear energy can be explained, quite simply, in terms of the transformation of energy from the vortex to the wave form.

Energy can be stored in matter and the key to understanding this potential energy is the vortex, because the vortex is a form of motion in which energy can be stored. Energy in motion is called kinetic energy. Just as the potential energy in mass can be converted into kinetic energy in an atomic explosion, so in nuclear physics, kinetic energy can be transformed back into mass.

When it rains in the Swiss Alps, water falls to form streams which tumble down the mountainsides. These join the torrent of rivers which pass through hydro-electric plants where the fall of the water is converted into the spin of the turbine and then the flow of electricity. Some of this electricity is fed into CERN, the European particle accelerator where it is used to accelerate protons. As the protons collide in the intersecting rings their motion is arrested and their kinetic energy is transformed into mass, as a host of new particles are created. As nothing was fed into the process apart from movement, common sense would suggest that these nuclear particles must be forms of movement. If this mass energy is treated as motion within the vortex - vortex energy - then it is easy to understand nuclear physics.

Nuclear physics began in 1896 when Henri Becquerel discovered radioactivity. Inspired by his discovery, Marie and Pierre Curie laboriously isolated a 1/5th gram of radium from a ton of uranium ore. In 1911, Rutherford purchased part of this radium and it was used to conduct the first true nuclear

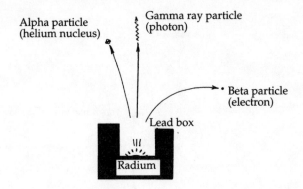

***Fig. 4.1*** *Natural radioactivity*

experiment. One of his students bombarded a thin film of gold with high energy *alpha particles* generated by the radium and Rutherford realised he had split the atom and revealed within it a small central nucleus.

High energy nuclear research came of age in physics with the discovery of cosmic rays. Cosmic rays consist of particles originating from high energy reactions in the sun and other stars. Generally, they are high velocity protons or, less frequently, alpha particles - the nuclei of helium atoms.

A pioneer of cosmic ray research was Professor Cecil Powell. of Bristol University. Just after World War II, he developed a special, 1mm thick, 80% silver bromide photographic emulsion for detecting cosmic ray reactions, and became renowned for littering the tops of Welsh mountains with stacks of photographic plates in black packets. Powell would leave them lying around for several weeks in the hope that a cosmic particle, penetrating the lightproof wrapping, would collide with the nucleus of an atom in the photographic emulsion. He chose mountain tops for his experiments because cosmic rays are more numerous on high ground than at sea level. By analysing the tracks left in the developed photographic plates, Powell was able to study the

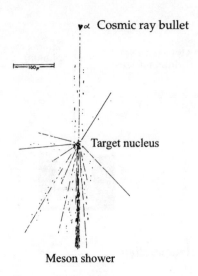

Fig. 4.2 *Pi-mesons*

results of high-energy sub-atomic reactions. He later improved on this amazingly simple and inexpensive form of high energy research by sending his photographic plates to the highest reaches of the atmosphere in weather balloons.

One of Powell's plates witnessed an alpha particle, with 3,000 billion *electron volts* of energy, colliding with the nucleus of an atom in the emulsion. A shower of 140 *pi-mesons* was created out of the arrested kinetic energy of the alpha particle. Within $10^{-8}$ sec. (one hundred millionth of a second), they reverted to radiant energy. The enormous importance of this experiment was that it showed that particles of matter could be formed out of movement - the arrested movement of the cosmic ray bullet. However, this wasn't why physicists throughout the world were jubilant about Powell's discovery: these were the mesons predicted by Yukawa, when he was a 28-year-old student at the Japanese University of Kyoto.

In 1936, the American researchers, Anderson and Neddermeyer, discovered a meson with a rest mass of 207 electron units, which came to be known as the *mu-meson*.

However, this didn't correspond to the Yukawa's predicted particle. But then Cecil Powell discovered the pi-mesons, or *pions*, that corresponded very closely to Yukawa's prediction. In their charged form, these rapidly decayed - within $10^{-8}$ sec. - into mu-mesons. Powell's mesons were obviously primary and for their discovery he shared the 1949 Nobel prize with Yukawa.

The production and decay of mesons can be understood from the Quantum Laws of Motion and the analogy of the coiled spring. If the proton is treated as a particle of vortex motion, then, as the kinetic energy of the cosmic ray particle passes through it, this arrested energy would be forced into vortex motion and so be transformed into mass. This would occur in keeping with the first Quantum Law of Motion. The wave-kinetic energy changed its state of motion from wave to vortex because it was forced to do so. The swirl of vortex energy would appear on the other side of the proton as a new, discrete particle of matter. However, this particle, identified as a meson, would be very short-lived because - in keeping with the second Quantum Law of Motion - once outside the proton there would be nothing to maintain the energy in vortex motion and so it would quickly revert to its original wave-kinetic form and radiate away. This could be likened to people that are arrested and sent to prison. They only remain as prisoners whilst they are retained by the prison walls. As soon as they are released they quickly revert to their free state again.

Meson production and decay can also be illustrated by an analogy of doughnuts. The proton vortex could be likened to the mould in a doughnut-making machine and the wave-kinetic energy to batter. The wave-kinetic energy forced through the proton vortex would emerge as a vortex particle in the same way that batter forced through a doughnut mould would come out in a doughnut shape. The energy would then revert to its original wave-kinetic form in the same way that the doughnut, if it were left uncooked, would quickly revert to a mass of batter.

The enormous stability of protons, against the instability of mesons and other newly discovered particles - which is a major problem with the quark theory - is the cornerstone of the vortex hypothesis. The stability of the proton could be taken as the ground of the first Quantum Law of Motion that: *Particles of energy maintain their form of motion unless a change is forced upon them.* The fact that the new particles produced from kinetic energy in the accelerators are so unstable could be taken as a vindication of the second Quantum Law of Motion that: *Once the force of change is removed then the particle of energy will revert to its original form.* Many of the results of high energy physics could be explained from these two simple laws of motion.

Cosmic ray research was very haphazard and the energy of cosmic rays could not be controlled, so physicists built particle accelerators in order to control and increase the energy of their bombarding particles. By passing ever increasing amounts of energy through atomic nuclei, they were able to create ever more massive particles. These particles could be explained as short-lived vortices forced into existence by the arrest of ever larger quantities of kinetic energy. In the terms of the doughnut analogy, particle accelerators could be described as multi-billion-dollar doughnut- making machines!

The rapid decay of the new particles would occur according to the second Quantum Law of Motion because the vortex form is not the natural state of motion of the wave-kinetic energy propelling the particle bullets in the accelerators. These short-lived phantom vortices would decay back into wave-kinetic energy as rapidly as possible. Any longevity would be due to a delay in the process of their unravelling from the unnatural vortex to their natural wave form again.

In high energy experiments, whilst some of the new particles decayed within $10^{-25}$ sec. (the time it took for light to traverse an atomic nucleus), others lasted far longer. Some, persisting for as long as $10^{-10}$ sec., were lasting more than a million times longer than expected. Because of their longevity, Murray Gell-Mann called them *strange particles* and *strangeness* came to be known as a fundamental property of matter.

Strange particles usually decay into more stable particles. Most leave behind them a proton or electron and sometimes even both. Strangeness could be a result of these stable, natural vortices acting to delay the operation of the second Quantum Law of Motion. This process could be understood from the analogy of hailstones.

A hailstone forms in a cloud as ice laminates around a seed of dust. The hailstone then falls from the cloud, melts and leaves the particle of dust behind. Similarly, as energy is forced through an atomic nucleus in a high energy reaction, it could form a short-lived vortex around a proton, neutron or electron and emerge as a new, unstable particle with a stable particle at its core. The swirling energy would then revert from vortex to wave and radiate away, leaving the stable particle seed behind. A delay in this transformation of unstable vortex to wave would be expected if the stable vortex at the core exerted a stabilising or holding influence over the unstable vortex of energy swirling around it.

Particles appear in accelerator experiments at critical mass-energy levels in much the same way that electrons occur in the atom at certain energy levels. This principle of discrete energy levels is fundamental to the quantum theory.

As physicists increase the energy in their accelerators they generate increasingly more massive particles at successive intervals. The massive particles could then decay in steps to reveal new, lighter particles at lower levels of energy where particles tend to appear. Several levels of mass energy, forming round a proton seed, would correspond to what physicists call *doses of strangeness*.

The decay of a particle in steps, to reveal lighter particles, is described in physics as *shedding doses of strangeness*. If the stable proton, at the core of the unstable strange particle, were to exert a holding influence over it, then as each dose of strangeness is shed, the holding influence over the residual particle would obviously be stronger. This would be because there would be less mass to

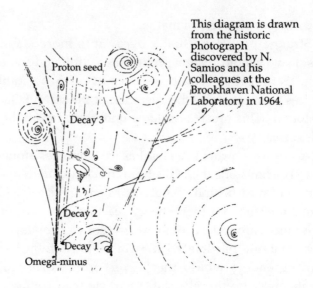

This diagram is drawn from the historic photograph discovered by N. Samios and his colleagues at the Brookhaven National Laboratory in 1964.

*Fig. 4.3   Cascade decay of the omega-minus*

stabilise and the swirling vortex energy would be closer to the stabilising core.  Consequently as each dose of strangeness is shed the new particle should possess a longer life span than the one that went before it.  This is illustrated in the *cascade decay* of a particle called the *omega-minus*.

In February 1964, at the Brookhaven National Laboratory in America, physicists witnessed the cascade decay of a new, heavy particle they called the omega-minus.  This particle had been predicted by Gell-Mann and its decay in three steps, shedding a dose of strangeness at each step, lent considerable support to the quark theory.  However, the decay of the omega-minus can also be used to substantiate the vortex explanation for strangeness which goes to show how one experiment can support two completely contradictory theories.

In the Brookhaven bubble-chamber photograph, after each successive decay step, the length of track was longer.  That indicated that each successive strange particle lasted longer than its predecessors.  (The cascade decay of the omega minus does not conform to the simple hailstone model. At each stage of the decay, vortex energy is shed as a new, discrete particle which travels off and decays into radiant energy after a short period of time. In terms of the hailstone model one would need to imagine a large hailstone shedding bits of ice, each melting in turn.)

However, it wasn't the appearance of the omega-minus so much as the results of a series of experiments performed in the mid-1960's at SLAC (the Stanford Linear Accelerator in California) that caused the quark theory to become accepted into mainstream physics. These also led to a Nobel prize for Murray Gell-Mann in 1969.

In the SLAC experiments, electrons were accelerated by intense radio pulses, down a three-kilometre-long 'vacuum tube' and then targeted on protons in liquid hydrogen. The results of these experiments showed that electrons were being scattered, or bounced back from the protons. From this it was inferred that protons contained smaller, hard particles.

The SLAC experiments, and their results, were reminiscent of those conducted by Lord Rutherford, when he bombarded the atoms in gold foil with alpha particles. Most of the particles passed right through the foil but some bounced back after colliding with small bodies inside the atom. Rutherford then

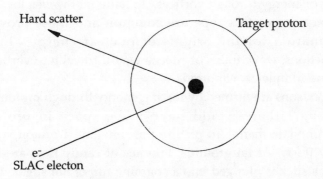

*Fig. 4.4* *The SLAC experiment*

went on to show that his bombarding particles were bouncing off protons. The SLAC experiments appeared to show that Rutherford's protons, in their turn, contained smaller, hard particles. The physicists at SLAC naturally concluded that their bombarding particles were bouncing off quarks. Their findings were subsequently confirmed at CERN, the European Nuclear Laboratory near Geneva. At CERN, protons were being accelerated in vast intersecting rings. At the intersections, energetic protons were directed into head-on collisions. In the high energy impacts, new particles were formed and came out at right angles to the beams. Again these results seemed to confirm the quark model. However, these experiments only demonstrated that *the proton has a hard heart*. They did not necessarily prove that it contains quarks. There could be an altogether different explanation for the hard heart of the proton.

If the proton were a spherical vortex then it could be treated as a system of increasingly compact lines of force. Bombarding particles would compress these lines of force, and being vortices themselves, would undergo reciprocal compression. The compression of increasingly compact lines of force would result in hard rather than soft impacts between the bombarding particles.

Nuclear physics has been mostly concerned with high energy interactions which could be understood in terms of forcing wave trains of energy through vortices. In nature, however, low energy interactions of this type are common and these provide an explanation for the origins of nuclear energy. In these interactions, wave trains of energy would travel into vortices and become completely captured.

If mesons are formed by forcing energy through protons, quite obviously there would have to be space in protons to accommodate them. To picture this, imagine a proton vortex as candy floss. At fairgrounds, bundles of candy floss are formed when a stick is plunged into a spinning tub of hot sugar. Strands of sugar get caught on the stick and are drawn round in a spiral path to form an open, lattice-like structure. This model represents the vortex with internal space. If the proton is a vortex with internal space, this space would obviously follow the curvature of the vortex and so any energy travelling into it would find itself in space with a spiral structure. Through the general theory of relativity, Einstein established that radiant energy follows the curvature of space and following the contour of spiral space, the captured energy would drive itself in toward the centre of the proton vortex.

The proton vortex could also be likened to a crab pot and travelling energy to a crab. The crab can enter the pot but then it can't escape. In the same way, the spiral structure of space within the proton would make it easy for energy to enter the vortex but practically impossible for it to leave again. The captured energy would then swirl around inside the proton or neutron indefinitely. If a proton or neutron vortex were treated as an energy trap, then in the same way that a crab pot takes no action to capture crabs, so a proton vortex would not act to capture energy. The pot is passive. It is the crab which crawls into it. In the same way, the proton vortex would be passive and the energy would move into it and so become captured. The crab trap captures crabs through the way it is structured. In like manner the proton would capture energy by reason of its structure which presents a spiral space-path to energy. A trap can continue to capture creatures until it is full. In the same way, a proton or neutron vortex could continue to capture energy until it is saturated with captured energy.

Protons and neutrons (collectively called *nucleons*) saturated with captured energy could also be likened to buckets full of water. If one bucket were placed inside the other the capacity to contain water would be reduced and so some of the water would spill out. In the same way, if two nucleons were to converge, their capacity to contain captured energy would be reduced and some of it would be evicted. The eviction of captured energy, due to the convergence of nucleons, provides an account for nuclear energy.

Captured energy would constitute part of the mass of the proton. This mass of captured energy would be represented by the pi-meson. If the mass of a pi-meson is equivalent to 270 electrons and the mass of a proton saturated with captured energy is 1836, then the mass of the proton vortex would be only 1566 *electron-mass units*. The loss of captured energy, due to the convergence of two protons - or neutrons - would be accompanied by a small loss in the mass of the protons. This would come from the partial destruction of the meson rather than the proton.

In the sun, protons converge to form helium nuclei. This process, called *nuclear fusion*, also occurs in the hydrogen bomb. As the protons fuse they lose 0.72% of their sum mass. This would be equivalent to a 4.9% loss of captured energy. The destruction of mass is accompanied by an equivalent release of nuclear energy.

Nuclear energy is also released in *nuclear fission*. In this process a large nucleus, such as that of uranium, splits to form the two smaller nuclei of strontium and xenon. Nuclear energy is released because protons and neutrons are more tightly bound in the smaller nuclei than in the uranium. The loss of mass and resultant release of nuclear energy is considerably less in nuclear fission than nuclear fusion.

The complete capture of wave-kinetic energy, by protons and neutrons, provides an explanation for the *strong nuclear force* as well as nuclear energy. When protons and neutrons converge to form an atomic nucleus they become bound together and the more they converge the more tightly bound do these nucleons become. This *nuclear binding* is called the strong nuclear force.

The strong nuclear force can be readily explained by the vortex. As nucleons converge, the captured energy would begin to swirl between them. The swirling of captured energy, around the centres of the two or more vortices, would act as a force to bind them together. Caused by captured energy, this force would operate over a range limited to the diameter of an atomic nucleus

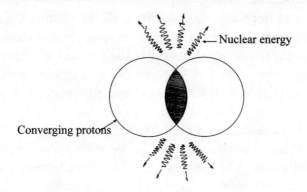

*Fig. 4.5  Nuclear energy*

- which would explain why the strong nuclear force is confined within the atomic nucleus.

If the vortices became more converged, the distance between their centres would decrease. The captured energy would then swirl in a shorter circuit which would bind them more tightly together. This would be accompanied by a proportionate loss of mass and release of nuclear energy as more captured energy is evicted. Because of this relationship between the loss of mass and increase in binding between nucleons, physicists have a formula which links mass loss to nuclear binding. However, in the vortex hypothesis the loss of mass is not linked to the binding of nuclear particles. The increase in binding results from the shorter path the binding energy travels between the two nucleon centres. This, and the loss of mass, are seen as quite separate consequences of the convergence of vortices saturated with captured energy. The link between mass loss and binding appears in nuclear fission and fusion because in these processes only a small percentage of the captured energy is evicted when the nucleons converge. Most of the captured energy remains in the nucleus to bind it together which more than compensates for the loss. However, if the loss of mass continued to a point where most of the captured energy were evicted, then the binding between the nuclear particles would begin to decrease. Eventually, if all the captured energy were evicted from a group of protons in an atomic nucleus, the nuclear binding would disappear and they would fall apart. If the pi-meson represents 15% of the mass of a proton then this would occur if 15% of the mass of each nucleon were to be destroyed.

Physicists have used the mathematical relationship between binding and mass to predict that as the mass of sub-nuclear particles continues to be destroyed, the binding between them would increase indefinitely. They think this is possible because, whilst they have the formulae, they do not have the fundamental understanding of nuclear energy and they have used this lack of understanding to shore up the quark theory. An awkward fact about quarks is that each of the three quarks in a proton has a mass five times greater than the proton itself. Richard Feynman recognised this as a problem when he said,"...the problem of the masses of the particles had been swept into a corner".

Physicists have dismissed the problem of quark mass by suggesting that in becoming bound into a proton the three quarks lost fourteen fifteenths of their sum mass. The resultant binding between the quarks was then so strong that a quark could never escape from a proton and that, they say, is why a quark has never been seen!

An experiment to prove that the binding between nuclear particles does not increase indefinitely with destruction of their mass would be another nail in the coffin of the quark theory. It would also show the mistake physicists have made in putting more emphasis on their mathematics than on their fundamental understandings of such things as nuclear energy.

The vortex account for nuclear energy and the strong nuclear force can be summarised in a hedgehog analogy. The proton vortex could be likened to a hedgehog and captured energy to fleas. Just as every hedgehog carries a resident population of fleas so every proton would carry captured energy. The hedgehog never did anything to acquire its fleas, they simply hopped on board. So the proton did nothing to acquire its captured energy; the wave-kinetic energy simply drove into the proton vortex.

If a hedgehog is weighed, the greater part of the measured weight would be that of the hog, but a lesser part would be that of its fleas. In like manner the greater part of the measured mass of a proton would be that of the stable proton vortex, but a lesser part would be that of the unstable swirl of captured energy it contains.

The total flea population would represent the meson particle. If the fleas were collected and weighed they would give an indication of the hedgehog's capacity for fleas. In the same way, the mass-energy of a pi-meson would represent the capacity of a proton to contain captured energy.

The hedgehog prickles could be taken to represent charge repulsion between protons. Because of their prickles hedgehogs only converge if they are pushed together. So it is that protons will only converge if they collide with considerable force. As the prickles of the two hedgehogs are pushed together there would be less space between them for fleas and so some of the fleas would be evicted. In the same way, as two protons converge there would be less space within them for captured energy and so some would be lost and would radiate away as nuclear energy.

With the loss of fleas, the weight of the converged hedgehogs would be less than the sum of their weights before they were brought together. So it is that the mass of two converged protons would be less than the sum of their masses before they collided.

Most of the fleas would remain on the hedgehogs and, not being bothered about which back they bite, would leap from hog to hog. In like manner captured energy, unconcerned within which vortex it swirls, would circulate between the converged protons.

If the exchange of fleas between two hedgehogs were taken to represent the strong nuclear force that binds protons and neutrons together, then the hedgehog analogy could be used to illustrate Yukawa's explanation for nuclear binding. However, the vortex explanation for mesons and the strong nuclear force does not require the assumption of arbitrary and inexplicable processes going on inside protons, which are hidden behind a shroud of uncertainty. Neither does it require that protons take any action, such as borrowing energy, in the formation of mesons and the nuclear binding force. The vortex offers an account for mesons as captured energy and in energy capture, protons are completely passive. They merely present a spiral space-path to wave-kinetic energy. The vortex explanation for the nuclear binding also makes it possible to dispense with the speculations that have grown around it in defence of the quark theory.

The formation of neutrons requires an explanation in terms of the vortex model. Neutrons are born in stars as a result of collisions between high energy electrons and protons. The electron vortex, driven by partially captured energy, could be visualised as smashing into a proton where it becomes enmeshed and held by the force of electric charge acting between them. In the neutron, the proton would immobilise the electron by virtue of its greater static inertia. Unable to undergo annihilation, because of the greater mass of the proton, and meeting the resistance of swirling captured energy within the proton vortex, the electron would come to rest just outside the region occupied by the completely captured energy. It could be pictured as lodging on the surface of the proton represented by the outermost range of the strong nuclear force -corresponding to the outermost region of the proton vortex capable of complete capture.

The kinetic energy of the electron - its partially captured energy - corresponding to 1.5 x its rest mass, would cause it to vibrate. Held to the proton by opposite charge attraction, but driven by its kinetic energy, one could imagine the electron 'bouncing' on the neutron. If one of the bounces were strong enough, the electron would escape from its electric bondage to the proton. The resultant spontaneous explosion of the high energy electron from the neutron would account for beta-decay, a major aspect of natural radioactivity.

In the 1920's, a serious problem arose in the study of beta decay. Physicists found that the electrons, emitted from radioactive atoms, emerged with a wide range of different energies, whereas the total available energy released from the neutron decay was the same on every occasion. The problem was trying to account for the energy lost from the nucleus when an electron emerged with less than this maximum amount of energy. Careful studies showed that the surplus energy was not appearing as heat, light or gamma rays. In 1930, Wolfgang Pauli suggested that another particle was released in the process of beta decay which carried away the excess energy. Fermi dubbed it the neutrino meaning "little neutral one". The neutrino is a mystery in physics but it isn't difficult to deduce what it is. It has neither mass nor charge so it cannot be a vortex. It is a form of radiant energy. So, because the photon is a form of radiant energy without mass, the neutrino appears to be more akin to a photon of light than a particle of matter. It has a value of quantum spin denoted by a half Planck's constant which means it must be a single quantum entity. It could be a radiant enetron. The neutrino could represent one half of a photon and an anti-neutrino could be the other half. It would seem that when an electron explodes out of a neutron it carries away only some of its partially captured energy. Using the tadpole analogy, one could imagine the electron wave-particle tearing away from the neutron and leaving part of its tail behind. This then escapes and radiates away, not as a photon but as a single enetron.

An interesting feature of neutrinos is that they are very penetrating. Neutrinos can pass right through the Earth without reacting with matter at all. The lack of interaction between neutrinos and matter suggests that enetrons only interact with vortices, through partial or complete capture, when they enter the tight spiral regions of space in or near a sub-atomic particle.

The atom is mainly space which is occupied by fields of electric charge, magnetism and gravity. Sub-atomic particles and atoms can interact with each other at a distance by means of these forces.  Photons of light are closely related to the electric and magnetic fields of matter and this would appear to enable them to interact with the force fields extending from particles of matter.  It could be for this reason that photons react readily with matter.  However, the fact that they can interact with electric and magnetic fields extending from particles of matter, does not mean that they are electro-magnetic fields, as theoretical physics would have us believe.  This becomes clear from the vortex account for electric charge and magnetism.

Chapter 5

# ELECTRIC CHARGE AND MAGNETISM

*"I believe that matter itself is just spin."*

*Eric Laithwaite*

Electric charge and magnetism are forces that act at a distance between bodies of matter to cause fragments of paper to leap onto a charged comb and bar magnets to bounce off each other without touching. *Action at a distance* has always perplexed scientists. How can two bodies of matter act on each other when there is nothing but space between them? Gravity, charge and magnetism act over vast distances. To explain them, classical scientists conceived of mysterious *force fields* permeating empty space until Einstein suggested that the action was a property of the space itself. The mysteries of electric charge, magnetism and gravity and their link with space can be resolved by the vortex hypothesis.

As far back as 600 BC, the Greeks discovered that if amber was rubbed with wool it would become charged and attract light-weight objects. The word electric is derived from the Greek word *elektron* for amber. An electric charge can be imparted on many objects by friction. It occurs when a comb is pulled through dry hair or when a nylon shirt is pulled off the back. It is caused by the accumulation of electrons that have been stripped by friction off atoms in the material.

The word magnet came originally from the name given to an ore of iron found near the ancient city of Magnesia. Fragments of this ore were observed to attract small pieces of metallic iron. It was found that this effect was most pronounced at particular areas on the stones, which came to be known as their poles. As early as 121 AD, the Chinese used lumps of magnetic ore to magnetise rods of iron. When suspended, these rods aligned themselves in the north-south direction and suspended magnets were used as aids to navigation in the West from the 11th century onwards. Because natural magnets were used for direction finding, they came to be known as *lode* stones from the old English for *way*.

In 1820 the Danish scientist, Hans Christian Oersted, first demonstrated a link between electricity and magnetism when he showed that an electric current in a wire could deflect a magnetic compass needle. Later, the English scientist Michael Faraday showed that a moving magnetic field would induce the flow of an electric current in a wire. This suggested that electricity and magnetism could be incorporated in a single theory. The Scots mathematician James Clerk Maxwell then developed the equations for electro-magnetism and went on to predict that light consisted of electro-magnetic fields radiating through space. This was based on his hunch that space was full of electricity. Then the German scientist Heinrich Hertz produced radio-waves from a high-frequency, alternating current of electricity. This fitted Maxwell's predictions precisely so scientists accepted his theory.

Maxwell's electro-magnetic theory is one of the few theories from 19th century physics which is held to be true in modern physics. However, for all its success it may not be correct and its success may be yet another example of the weakness in the scientific method. Because Maxwell's prediction was vindicated by experiment, his idea came to be accepted as fact. But Hertz's experiment didn't prove that radio-waves were electro-magnetic waves. It merely showed that alternating electric and magnetic fields could radiate energy in wave form. The fact that these radio-waves, in their turn, could induce a flow of electricity in a wire - the principle behind radio - merely proved that energy in the form of light and radio-waves can interact with the electric and magnetic fields associated with particles of matter. The experiments demonstrated the interactions between photons and electric and magnetic fields. They didn't prove that photons of light are electro-magnetic fields.

Maxwell was an outstanding scientist and the model he developed for light, as a pair of waves moving at right angles, has been an immense contribution to physics, but by labelling them as *electro-magnetic* I believe that he set physicists on a false trail of unification. Throughout the 20th Century physicists have endeavoured to unify matter and light in the same field theory and these attempts have been fuelled by wave-particle duality and wave-mechanics. With light acting as though it were formed of particles and matter behaving like waves it is hardly surprising that most physicists have followed this trail and are likely to resist the idea that matter and light are composed of two fundamentally different forms of energy.

The reason why a clear difference between light and matter is not apparent to scientists is because the wave form of energy interacts with the vortex. With the vortex acting as an energy trap it is unlikely that 'singleton' vortices occur in nature. It is more likely that naturally occurring particles will be 'marriages' of wave and vortex. The lack of distinction between wave and vortex would obviously lead to wave-particle duality and unified field theories embracing both matter and light and mask the fact that they are based on fundamentally different forms of energy.

Maxwell's concept, that light consisted of electric and magnetic fields, was reversed by Richard Feynman. Feynman suggested that the electric and magnetic fields of matter were created by particles of light. His concept was that periodically particles of light would pop up alongside charged particles. These were exchanged with another charged particle and then

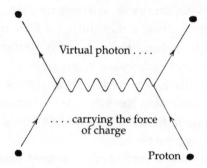

*Fig. 5.1 Feynman diagram*

vanished again. The whole process of the light appearing and disappearing occurred within the bounds of Heisenberg's uncertainty principle and so the particles could never be detected experimentally. For this reason they were called *virtual photons* of light.

One could imagine broadsides of virtual photons being fired between charged particles as though they were minute battleships. These energetic interactions were thought to be responsible for pushing them apart or pulling them together.

Feynman designed diagrams to illustrate the exchange of virtual photons. These *Feynman diagrams* have also been used to illustrate the exchange of other force-carrying particles.

The concept that force-carrying particles could be exchanged over large distances met with difficulties. Once a force-carrying particle was launched into space how did it locate its target particle at a distance? This was essential if it was to cause an interaction and undergo the demise necessary for the debt of energy, incurred in its formation, to be repaid. The meticulous accounting of the universal energy bank didn't allow for any force-carrying particles to be lost in space.

To overcome this difficulty a new theory was introduced which suggested that force-carrying particles could *gauge* the force, that is they could feel for the presence of another force-carrying particle and so home in on their target. This ability of force carrying particles to feel each other was illustrated by an adaptation of Feynman's original diagram. In my opinion, the weakness of this gauge theory is that it heaps speculation on speculation by attributing arbitrary properties to particles which are themselves arbitrary properties of particles.

However, whatever the explanation, if energy exchanges between particles are held responsible for electric charge this raises an immediate problem. In the words of the physicist Harald Fritzsch, "We do not understand why the neutron is heavier than the proton. Indeed an unbiased physicist would have to assume the opposite by the following logic. It is reasonable to think that the difference in mass between the proton and neutron is related to electro-magnetic interaction since the proton has an electric field and the neutron does not. If we rob the proton of its charge, we would expect the neutron and the proton to have the same mass. The proton is therefore logically expected to be heavier than the neutron by an amount corresponding to the energy needed to create the electric field around it."

The vortex provides a completely new and refreshingly simple explanation for charge and magnetism. Because vortices are dynamic, should they overlap they would obviously interact. Vortex interactions could provide an account for the forces of electric charge and magnetism.

To begin with, vortices are innately dynamic and if electric charge were an expression of the active nature of the vortex there would be no requirement for any additional energy to account for charge interactions. The vortex hypothesis does not require that protons be more massive than neutrons.

To understand vortex interactions and action at a distance, imagine you were small enough to live in a vortex. You might experience it as a fireball. As you moved outward from the fiery centre, the energy would rapidly diminish. Suddenly it would appear to vanish altogether as though you had come to the end of the vortex and broken out of its fiery domain. However, the apparent surface of your vortex would not be its boundary, rather it would be merely the last intensity of energy that you could perceive. Looking out from this point into the darkness, you would see other fiery vortices moving about. It would be natural for you to assume that all these spinning balls of fire were separate vortices, occupying a void of darkness - like stars in the dark sky. However, your senses would be deceiving you. The apparent void of darkness would be full of energy extending from all the vortices. As the invisible energy from one vortex overlapped that of another, there would be an interaction between them. Standing on your ball of fire, seeing nothing but a void between the fireballs, you would obviously be perplexed at the inexplicable attractions and repulsions between them and speak of action at a distance.

As vortices of energy, sub-atomic particles of matter would be intrinsically dynamic and have no bounding surface - apart from the limits to complete capture in the proton or the neutron. The vortex energy, extending beyond our concept of perception, would interact with vortex energy extending from other vortices we imagine to be separate from it. This would create in our minds the phenomenon of action at a distance.

It cannot be said that matter is the vortex energy we perceive with our senses and the field of force is vortex energy extending beyond the bounds of our perception. We only perceive matter through its force fields. When we bump into a solid object we are perceiving a rigid atomic structure held together by the forces between the charged particles in the atoms. When we touch something we perceive only the repulsion forces between electric charges in the object and charges in the atoms of our hand. We perceive the vortex, not as a material entity, but through its interactions with other vortices. This illustrates the principle that quantum entities can only be perceived through their interactions.

A force field - such as electric charge - is an aspect of matter. If a particle of matter is a vortex, the field of force would be the

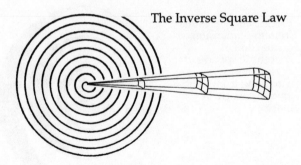

*Fig. 5.2 The Inverse Square Law*

effect of the vortex extending within and beyond the bounds of what we perceive to be matter. As the vortex extends out in all directions the drop in intensity of vortex energy would obey the *Inverse Square Law* for any extension in three dimensions - that is, the intensity of energy at any distance from the centre of the vortex would be inversely proportional to the square of that distance. If two vortices were to interact, their interaction would be proportional to the intensity of vortex energy involved in the interaction, which would be inversely proportional to the square of the distance between them. This would explain *Coulomb's Law*, named after the French scientist Charles Coulomb who, in the eighteenth century, first observed that the force of interaction between charges is inversely proportional to the square of the distance between them.

Another French scientist, Charles du Fey, described the two opposite types of charge, *positive* and *negative*. But why should there be only two types of charge and not three or four or more? In physics it is simply accepted that this is so. The vortex hypothesis can show why it is so. In the spherical vortex there are only two ways in which energy can flow - into or out of the centre. This property of the vortex would account for the opposite signs of charge. Positive charge is taken to represent the flow of energy out of the centre of the vortex and negative charge represents the flow into the centre.

Electric charge results from the expansion or contraction of concentric spheres of vortex energy, extending from a sub-atomic particle of matter.

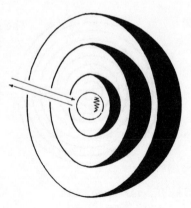

***Fig. 5.3*** *Electric charge*

Each vortex of energy represents an indivisible unit of charge interaction. As such, it should be treated as an irreducible *quantum of electric charge.* If charged particles are vortices of energy, they would all have the same unitary electric charge regardless of mass or any other property they might possess. A measured electric charge could only build up as an integer multiple of units of charge, each representing the action of a vortex of energy and this is precisely how electric charge accumulates - by the addition of more charged particles. Elementary particles have never been observed with charge greater or lesser than unity, which supports the vortex hypothesis and throws further doubt on the quark theory as quarks are supposed to possess fractional charge.

The vortex model also provides an explanation for the way charged particles interact. The flow of energy in the spherical vortex would take the form of concentric spheres either growing out of, or shrinking into the centre of the vortex. This means that the movement in the vortex responsible for the interactions of electric charge would be effective along its radii. This movement could be represented by *radial vectors.* Diagrams of the radial vectors of positive and negative charges can be overlaid to represent two interacting vortices of energy. The points of interaction of their radial vectors can then be plotted to derive the

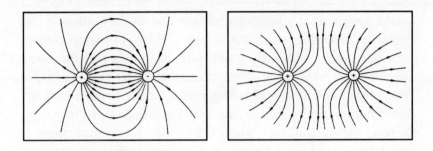

**Fig. 5.4** *Electric fields*

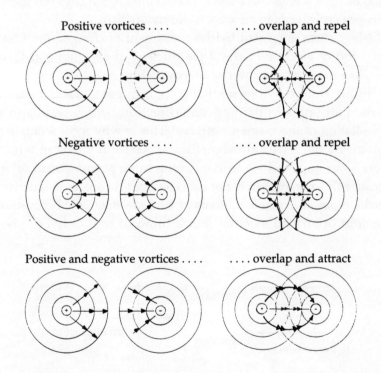

**Fig. 5.5** *Interacting vortices creating electric fields*

lines of force acting between them. From these lines of force it would appear that when vortices act against each other in the opposite direction - *anti-directional* - then repulsion occurs between them. When they act with each other in the same direction - *uni-directional* - then attraction occurs between them. This would explain why *like charges repel and unlike charges attract*. When the energy in two interacting vortices is uni-directional there is attraction, but when it is anti-directional there is repulsion. Mid-way between movement in the same and opposite direction is movement at right angles. Mid-way between attraction and repulsion is the state of zero interaction. It follows therefore that if two systems of vortex energy were to cross at right angles there should be no interaction between them. This principle leads to an account for magnetism.

Magnetism is created by the movement of charged particles. The orbit of electrons around the nucleus of an atom and their spin-like minute tops give rise to magnetism.

In the atom electrons normally occur in pairs. Each member of the pair spins in the opposite direction, which results in a cancellation of the magnetic effects. This is why most atoms are non-magnetic. Natural magnetism arises from atoms in which there is an unpaired electron spinning in an asymmetrical orbit. Because this magnetism is not cancelled out it confers magnetism on the atom as a whole. Atoms of iron are magnetic because of the spin of an odd electron, but a lump of iron only becomes

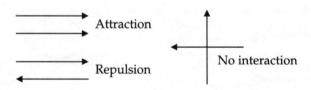

*Fig. 5.6 Directional rules for vortex interactions*

magnetic when the atoms are aligned in the same direction. If the atoms lose their alignment, which can occur through heating or hammering the lump of iron, then it loses its magnetism.

The spin of an electron creates a unit of magnetism called its *magnetic moment*. This, the basic unit of natural magnetism, can be explained by the vortex. If an electron is a vortex of energy, treated as a system of concentric spheres, its charge would be the flow of these spheres into its centre - a movement that would be effective along their radii. The magnetic moment of the electron would be the spin of these concentric spheres of vortex energy. This rotation would be effective at a tangent to the surface of each concentric sphere. Because a tangent to a sphere lies at right angles to its radii, the rotation of vortex energy responsible for the magnetic moment of an electron would be effective at right angles to the flow of vortex energy responsible for its charge. This explains why a magnetic field occurs at right angles to the electric field which forms it. Occurring at right angles these two motions of vortex energy are quite distinct and create separate force fields.

To understand the difference between charge and magnetism think of whirlpools and tops. The spin of water in a whirlpool represents charge and the spin of a top represents magnetism. Now imagine a whirlpool rotating in a strong tidal current. This illustrates three types of motion in the one system. The radial flow of the concentric spheres of energy is the primary movement of the vortex. This movement gives rise to electric charge and the

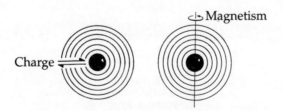

***Fig. 5.7*** *The difference between electric charge and magnetism*

form of the vortex itself. The vortex can then rotate. This secondary movement gives rise to its magnetic moment. The rotating vortex can then vibrate back and forth or move in a wavy line. These tertiary motions would be superimposed upon the primary and secondary movements of the vortex. If superimposed movements of the vortex are effective along its radii, they would add or detract from the force of charge. If, however, they are effective at a tangent to the vortex, the tangential movements would not interact with the charge. Instead they would establish the distinct set of interactions which have come to be associated with magnetism.

The laws of interaction applying to radial movements of vortex energy could also be applied to the tangential movements. When two systems of tangentially moving vortex energy act against each other in opposition, then their anti-directional motion would set up a force of repulsion between them. The force of repulsion between two electrons spinning in the same direction would arise from the fact that their rotating vortex energy is anti-directional where it overlaps and interacts. When two systems of tangentially moving vortex energy act with each other in unison, then their uni-directional motion would set up a force of attraction between them. The force of attraction between

Electrons spinning in the same direction repel because of the . . .

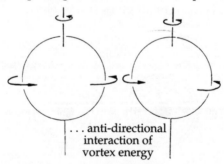

. . . anti-directional
interaction of
vortex energy

*Fig. 5.8 Repulsion between electrons spinning in the same direction*

Electrons spinning in opposite direction attract because of the . . .

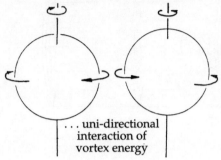

. . . uni-directional
interaction of
vortex energy

***Fig. 5.9*** *Attraction between electrons spinning in opposite direction*

two electrons spinning in opposite direction would arise from the fact that their rotating vortex energy is uni-directional where it overlaps and interacts.

An electric current is surrounded by concentric cylinders of magnetism. This effect can be readily explained with the vortex model. At right angles to the direction of flow of the electrons in an electric current, the motion is effective at a tangent to their concentric spheres of vortex energy. Each moving electron would thus be surrounded by concentric rims of magnetism. The concentric rims of magnetism of all the electrons in the current would add up to form concentric cylinders of magnetism.

If two current-carrying conductors are laid side by side they will attract if the current is flowing in the same direction, but repel if it is flowing in the opposite direction. This effect was first observed by the French scientist Ampère. It occurs because the concentric rims of vortex energy are anti-directional between the currents flowing in opposite directions and are uni-directional between the currents flowing in the same direction.

Michael Faraday discovered that a stationary magnetic field would not interact with an electric field. However, he found that if a magnet was moved toward a wire it would induce a current of electricity within it. He used this discovery to invent a

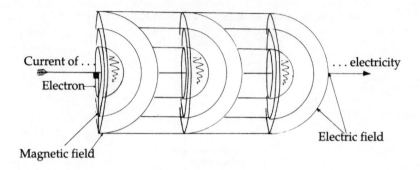

Current of . . .     . . . electricity

Electron

Electric field

Magnetic field

***Fig. 5.10*** *Electro-magnetism*

rudimentary dynamo and thus he paved the way for generating electricity.

The movement of a magnetic field is a tertiary motion of the vortex. If it occurs at right angles to the magnetic field then it would be radial in effect and so would interact with an electric field. In fact, when a magnetic field is moved it produces an electric field at right angles to the direction of motion.

Faraday also discovered that a growing or decaying magnetic field would interact with an electric field. This occurs because, in a growing or decaying magnetic field, the intensity of vortex energy is changing. Whilst the intensity of energy, in the vortex, is uniform over the surface of each concentric sphere, it varies along the radius. Uniform movements at a tangent to these spheres would not incur any change in intensity of vortex energy. This would be characteristic of a magnetic field. However, movements along the radii would be associated with change in intensity of vortex energy. This would be characteristic of an electric field, therefore any changes in intensity of vortex energy would be effective as charge rather than magnetism.

If magnetism is created by secondary motions superimposed upon the vortex, then the effects of its primary motion should be paramount. For example, if the direction of the primary motion setting up its charge were reversed, then the magnetic effect

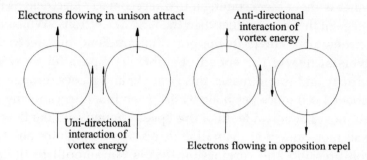

*Fig. 5.11* *Attraction and repulsion between flowing electrons*

would be reversed. Particles with the same sign of charge, but spinning in opposite direction, experience a magnetic attraction. If the sign of charge were reversed then the magnetic effect between them would become a force of repulsion.

This is apparent in a dance between electrons and positrons, called *positronium*, just prior to their annihilation. If the electron and positron are rotating in the same direction, then they attract each other and annihilate sooner. If, however, they are rotating in opposite direction they will repel and this delays their annihilation.

This section on electro-magnetism would not be complete without an account for electricity. I draw a parallel between electricity and sound. If sound is defined as 'longitudinal vibrations in matter', rather than just the vibrations we hear, then electricity fits this definition.

Electricity is produced by the longitudinal vibrations of electrons in matter. When electrons are free to move, in a conductive substance, they can be aligned by the application of a potential gradient across the conductor. Once they are aligned, movement can be transmitted, from one electron to another, down the voltage gradient - the electrons could be imagined as shunting against each other. Because of their electric fields, the shunt, or longitudinal vibration, passes from one electron to another without them coming into direct contact. Electricity is the passage of this shunt rather than the flow of electrons. Whilst the electrons drift slowly in the potential gradient, the electricity travels at nearly the speed of light. The parallel between electricity and sound makes this clear. Sound passes through air at about 1,000 miles per hour whilst, even in a hurricane, the air itself moves at only a tenth of this speed. Sound isn't the flow of the air molecules; it is a vibration that passes through the air. It is a compression and rarefaction that is tantamount to the air molecules shunting and, like sound, electricity is the passage of activity through a medium rather than the passage of the medium itself. Sound involves the vibration of atomic matter whereas electricity involves the vibration of electrons, which are sub-atomic matter; so I like to think of electricity as *sub-atomic sound.*

Chapter 6

# SPACE, TIME
# AND GRAVITY

*"The most impressive fact is that gravity is simple."*

*Richard Feynman*

Most people assume that space is the emptiness left behind when matter is removed, but Einstein, thinking differently from most people, believed that space was not an absolute void. He treated it as something real and connected to matter. The importance of this thinking in regard to relativity is clear from a cryptic remark he made when he arrived in New York, in 1919. When asked by a reporter to explain his theory of relativity in a single sentence, he replied: "Remove matter from the Universe and you also remove space-time."

Einstein's original thinking about space began when he was only five. He was recovering from an illness and his father gave him a compass to play with. As he turned the compass, the needle kept pointing in the same direction. It struck the young Einstein that space must be holding the needle. Playing with the compass, Einstein conceived of the idea that space wasn't nothingness but was something as real as matter itself. It was this thinking that led him to his theories of relativity.

The vortex model provides a clear picture of space as a real form of energy. As energy in the vortex extends from the centre outward, its intensity would rapidly diminish to infinitesimal levels but would never reach zero, because zero is approached but never reached by dividing something into ever smaller fractions.

To understand this principle, imagine you had a balloon that never burst. If you kept blowing it up, the rubber would become infinitesimally thin and the balloon would become infinitely large but the total amount of rubber would always remain the same - it would simply be stretched over a larger and larger area. In the same way, vortex energy would not vanish into nothingness even though it extends out into infinity. It follows that every vortex must be as big as the Universe.

I believe that the extension of the vortex into infinity is what we know as space. The vortex creates the three-dimensional extension characteristic of space. This explains why space is an infinite extension and why it occurs in three dimensions rather than two or four or more. The fact that matter is also a three-dimensional extension strongly suggests a connection between matter and space.

Einstein saw space as something real that was connected to matter and distorted by matter. With the vortex, it is possible to go a step further and suggest that space and matter are one and the same thing. Space is not something connected to matter or distorted by matter because there is no physical difference between matter and space. They are both vortex energy. The difference between them occurs only in the mind of man. Matter is vortex energy we perceive and space is vortex energy extending beyond the limits of our perception - which is why it appears to us to be a void.

If the vortex is responsible for both matter and space, because matter is divided into particles, then space must also be discontinuous. The dense centre of the vortex would constitute the particle of matter and the sparse peripheral regions of the vortex would constitute its space. If a vortex is destroyed then a particle of matter and a part of space would disappear from existence. Thus, if matter is removed from the Universe, space is removed with it.

I visualise bodies of matter surrounded by bubbles of space occurring as an extension of their shape. These concentric bubbles of space would extend from the particle into infinity - each bubble fading away in intensity as it increases in size. At a distance from the body the intensity of energy contributed by its own bubble of space would be negligible. However, the summation of the bubbles arising from neighbouring particles would step up the intensity of space in that region. Space could be pictured as foam made up from the addition of all the bubbles of space reaching out from every particle and body of matter in existence. Concentric bubbles of space, extending from the Earth, the Sun and other planets and stars, would add up to form universal space.

Space bubbles would share, with elementary particles of matter, all the properties of the vortex. In fact, forces such as gravity, electric charge and magnetism would be more the property of space than the particles of which they are an extension, because they are merely effects of the vortex extending out to infinity. Space is active electrically and only appears to be electrically neutral because there are an equal number of opposite charges in existence. Space is also magnetically active. The Earth's magnetic field is a property of the space extending from the Earth. The five-year-old Einstein was right in assuming it was space that influenced the compass needle. The assumption that space is a void occupied by magnetic forces is just another myth that everyone has come to believe in. Magnetism appears to be a force field occupying space because one bubble of space occupies another. In the vortex hypothesis, magnetism is just the effect of one bubble of electrically active space rotating inside another.

Once it is appreciated that space is divided into parts - like everything else in the Universe - then it should be possible to include it in the quantum theory. The space bubble, extending from each particle of matter, could be described as a *quantum of space*.  The inclusion of space in the quantum theory provides a bridge between quantum theory and the theories of relativity. The quantum concept for space also leads to the resolution to some of the riddles of relativity.  In his special theory of relativity, Einstein predicted that space and time are relative to movement at the speed of light - which sets up a riddle: *How can space and time be relative to a speed of movement when speed is itself a relationship between space and time?*  It is a chicken and egg dilemma: *What came first, space-time or movement?*  This riddle of relativity is resolved if each vortex, as a particle of space and matter, exists and moves in the space created by another vortex. Each vortex would be a system of movement existing relative to all other vortices acting as space.  They would all be relative to the speed of light because that is the speed of motion underlying them all.  This principle also resolves the dilemma of how a vortex can both extend in three dimensions and create three dimensions.  Each vortex extends in the three dimensions created by other vortices.

I circumscribe quantum theory and relativity in the single principle that: *Energy is divided into parts and each is a particle of activity relative to all the other parts.*  This principle leads to the law that: *Each part of the Universe depends upon every other part for its existence.*  The mutual interdependence of every part of the Universe gives rise to the principle that: *Every part acts for the whole* and leads to the Universal ideal: *Love your neighbour as yourself.*

The vortex account for space provides a ready explanation for the key principle in the special theory of relativity that: *The observed velocity of light is independent of the velocity of the observer.*

An observer can only measure the speed of those photons of light which reach him.  As they do so they would be travelling in his own bubble of space.  Because this moves with him wherever he goes, his measure of the speed of light would be independent of his own movement toward or away from the source of light.

When Michelson and Morley conducted their classic

experiment in 1887, they found that the measured velocity of light was independent of the movement of the Earth. This was because the velocity of light was being measured relative to the bubble of space extending from the Earth. As this was moving with the Earth, their measurement of the velocity of light was not affected by the movement of the Earth.

Einstein had a different explanation. He believed that the speed of light is always the same, regardless of the motion of the observer, because space shrinks as the observer moves. For example, from the consideration of relative velocity, we might expect that light emitted from a body, approaching an observer at 100,000 miles per second would appear to have a velocity of 186,000 + 100,000 = 286,000 miles per second. But Einstein's special theory tells us that the 'mile' on a body moving at 100,000 miles/sec., is shorter than a stationary mile so that the light does not travel as 'far' in one second from the moving body and its velocity again works out at 186,000 miles/sec.

Einstein's concept that space contracts with acceleration does, however, work with the vortex. If space is created by the vortex, then the size of space would be a function of the size of the concentric spheres of energy forming the vortex. Near its centre these would be very small, but far from the centre of the vortex the spheres would be vast. Therefore the acceleration down the radius of the vortex, toward its centre, would be accompanied by a contraction of space.

The contraction or expansion of space occurs if we move in all three dimensions of space simultaneously. We experience this very real dimension of space when we grow. This is the dimension of size. I named it the *Alician Dimension*, after Alice - from *Alice in Wonderland* - who travelled by shrinking in this dimension, into a 'looking-glass world'.

Einstein included time in his theories of relativity, believing that time intervals grow longer as the observer moves. Einstein also treated time as a fourth dimension - existing as a continuum with the three dimensions of space. However, in the vortex hypothesis, time is treated merely as the relationship between things. Time is linked to space, only insofar as it is the relationship between one bubble of space and another. Every movement or change in the Universe exists as a sequence of events relative to the other processes that are occurring around it. This interdependence of events in our world is what we experience as time. Each process takes time from other repeating physical processes occurring around it. For example, we take our measure of time from the regular movements of the Earth. The spin of the Earth on its axis gives us our days and its orbit round the sun gives us our years.

Once you appreciate time as events going on around you, then you can see how it would appear to dilate, should you accelerate. If you were to accelerate, the surrounding flow of events - your clock - would appear to slow down. If these processes were using you as their clock then, as a result of your acceleration, their time would appear to speed up. Imagine you had a twin and you and your twin were the only things in existence. Your twin would be to you, space and time. He, in his turn, would depend upon you for his space and time. Each of you would be space-time to the other. If you were to accelerate, from your point of view, he, as your time, would have slowed down. From his point of view, you, as his time, would have speeded up. Einstein expressed this variance of time with acceleration in his famous *Twin Paradox*. In Einstein's story the twin who underwent an acceleration grew more slowly in the dilated time and therefore lived longer than the other twin. This longevity caused by acceleration is borne out by the increased lifespan of particles undergoing acceleration in particle accelerators. At CERN, for example, unstable *muons* (heavy electrons) accelerated to nearly the speed of light have survived nearly 30 times longer than muons at rest.

The ultimate source of time must be the relative movements between the most fundamental forms of energy. For example, the flow of energy in one vortex, as a repeating sequence of events, would exist as a clock for the flow of energy in another vortex and vice versa. The acceleration toward the centre of the vortex would also affect time. If you were using a vortex as a clock, then, with acceleration toward the centre, you would experience a dilation of time. If, like Alice, you were to suddenly shrink into the realms of smaller space, then the minutes of your normal experience would first become hours, then days, then years, as you accelerated in toward the centre of the vortex. At atomic size, the seconds of time measured by normal people would seem like years. If, however, you were to grow into a giant, capable of leaping from star to star, as you looked down on the planet Earth you would see it spinning like a top and whizzing around the sun. Days would appear as minutes and years as mere hours. If you were to continue growing, human days would become your seconds, and years your minutes. If you were to grow until you were big enough to look down on the Universe, as though it were a football, its lifespan of billions of terrestrial years could well seem like a week to you.

In his general theory of relativity, Einstein used the slowing of time, with acceleration, in a very ingenious way. He suggested that if acceleration resulted in the slowing down of time then the slowing down of time should appear as an acceleration. He used this idea to explain gravity.

Einstein suggested that space and time formed a single, four-dimensional continuum. He then went on to speculate that this was distorted by matter. The distortion manifested as a curvature of space and an extension of time intervals. It is hard to picture this, but Einstein used the image of a sheet of rubber as space-time and a heavy ball as a massive body of matter. The ball would stretch the rubber and cause a dip in it. The stretching of the sheet represents the stretching of time and the dip represents the curvature of space. As another ball enters the dip it would roll in the curve toward the first ball. This represents gravity, the acceleration of the second body of matter toward the first in the curved space-time.

Einstein suggested that this gravitational effect occurred not because the object entered a gravitational force field, but because it entered a region in which space-time was distorted by another body of matter. The result of entering a region where time slowed down would be that the object would appear to accelerate. Einstein indicated that the energy of acceleration would come from the destruction of mass. He dismissed the idea of force fields altogether on the grounds that it is impossible to show by experiment whether a force is caused by a force field or an acceleration. He called this *the principle of equivalence of forces*.

This principle is self-evident. The occupants of a rocket ship fall toward its rear it accelerates. If, on its return to Earth, the rocket were to free-fall in the Earth's gravitational field, its occupants would experience weightlessness. The occupants of the rocket ship would have no way of distinguishing between gravity acting as a force field and the acceleration of their rocket ship. Einstein concluded that, likewise, we on Earth could not be certain whether gravity was the result of an acceleration or a force field.

However, whilst Einstein may have dismissed Newton's view that gravity was the result of interacting force fields in favour of the effect of relative accelerations, and whilst many people

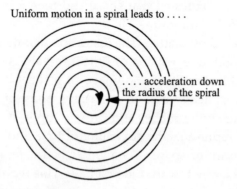

Uniform motion in a spiral leads to . . . .

. . . . acceleration down the radius of the spiral

*Fig. 6.1 Acceleration in the vortex*

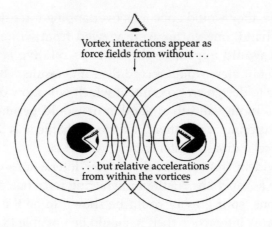

Vortex interactions appear as
force fields from without . . .

. . . but relative accelerations
from within the vortices

**Fig. 6.2** *The principle of equivalence of forces.*

believe that he has thereby toppled Newton, the principle of
equivalence of forces does not allow this. The principle demands
that Newton and Einstein both *be correct* in their differing points
of view. If the principle of equivalence is valid then a complete
theory for gravity has to encompass the views of both Newton
and Einstein, showing each to be but an opposite side of the same
coin. In the vortex hypothesis this is achieved.

A feature of the vortex is that it presents itself to all other
vortices as a system of acceleration. This is a result of it being
motion in a spiral. Uniform motion in a spiral results in an
acceleration down the radius of the spiral. This principle can be
illustrated by a two-dimensional spiral such as a spool of tape on
a tape-recorder. As the tape winds off the spool at a uniform
speed, the spool accelerates.

If two spheres are placed in contact they touch at the point of
a radius. Spherical vortices will always connect with each other
radially, therefore each will be, to the other, a system of
accelerating motion. Because of this, radial vortex interactions
can be treated equally as relative accelerations or interacting force
fields depending upon the observer's point of view.

In charge interactions, for example, if two vortices are viewed from above, they would appear as overlapping force fields. If, on the other hand, one vortex were viewed from within the other then each would appear to the other as relative acceleration. Either point of view would record the same results. Because it is impossible to design an experiment which will show one point of view to be more valid than another, it would be impossible to show by experiment whether the force of charge was the result of relative accelerations or interacting force fields.

It is evident from charge that vortex interactions can show a force to be as much the result of interacting force fields as relative accelerations, so if gravity could be shown to be the result of a similar vortex interaction then it should be possible to provide an explanation for gravity that upholds the principle of equivalence of forces.

With the vortex hypothesis it is possible to overcome obvious difficulties which Sir Isaac Newton saw in trying to explain the action of one body of matter on another at a distance, due to gravity. In a letter to his friend, Richard Bentley, Newton wrote: "...It is inconceivable that inanimate brute matter should, without the mediation of something else which is not material, operate upon and affect other matter without mutual contact..."

The vortex model depicts particles of matter as neither inanimate nor brute and because of the infinite extension of the vortex, particles of matter are never out of mutual contact. If gravity were the result of a vortex interaction, there would be no need to assume the existence of a mediating, non-material force to account for it, because the vortex is both the particle and the force field extending from it.

When Newton invented the concept of gravity he was sitting in an orchard pondering on the fall of an apple. Prior to its fall the apple wasn't moving, it was attached to a tree. Something must have been pulling on it to cause it to become detached and then move toward the Earth. Newton argued that the same pull must be acting on all bodies of matter to draw them together. He suggested that this pull would explain the orbits of the moon and planets. His theory was very successful but not as accurate as Einstein's. Newton's theory could not account for the precession of planetary orbits - most notable in the orbit of Mercury - but this was because Newton's theory did not allow for the curvature of space. Gravity acting through curved space provides a full account for planetary orbits.

The vortex hypothesis provides an account for curved space but this is very different from Einstein's. Einstein based his theory for gravity on the assumption that matter distorts space-time. In the vortex model, the curvature of space results from its being an extension of matter rather than something that is distorted by matter.

The vortex explanation for the curvature of space shows the same effects on light as Einstein's description. Einstein predicted that the distortion of space-time around the sun would cause an apparent curvature of star-light as it passes through the 'dip'. The vortex hypothesis shows that star-light would follow a curved path as it passes through the vast bubble of space extending from the sun.

Both Einstein and Newton's theories for gravity are weak because they contain arbitrary assumptions. Einstein assumed that matter distorts space-time in order to explain gravity whilst Newton assumed that gravity was caused by something non-material acting between bodies of matter. Einstein never gave a clear picture of what space-time was so that it could be distorted by matter, and Newton never left a clue as to what the mysterious non-material entity was that acted between bodies of matter to pull them together.

The vortex hypothesis provides a unified description of space, time and matter. They are all aspects of the vortex. Because the vortex is curved, space is curved. Because the vortex extends beyond our direct perception, bodies of matter can act on each other at a distance. Because the vortex is intrinsically dynamic these interactions can occur without the mediation of any non-material entities. Thus no arbitrary assumptions are required in

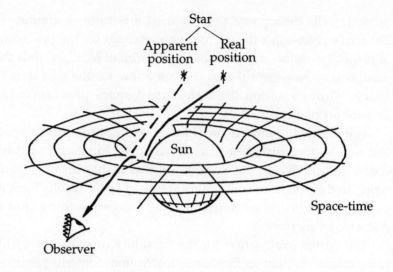

*Fig. 6.3 Einstein's account for space-time curvature*

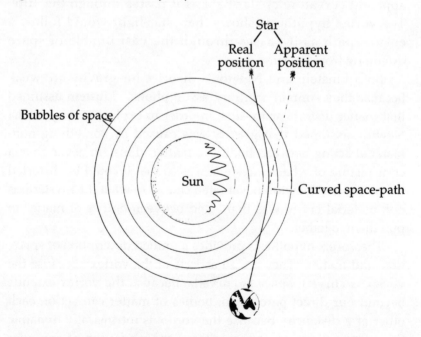

*Fig. 6.4 The vortex account for curved space*

| Gravity | Quantum Space |
|---|---|
| 1. Force associated with matter. | 1. Extension of matter. |
| 2. Acts from the centre of each particle of matter. | 2. Extends from the centre of each particle of matter. |
| 3. Unlimited range. | 3. Unlimited extension. |
| 4. Obeys the Inverse Square Law in action. | 4. Obeys the Inverse Square Law in extension. |
| 5. Causes the path of light to be curved. | 5. Causes the path of light to be curved. |
| 6. Universal gravity is the sum of the components of gravity acting from countless particles of matter. | 6. Universal gravity is the sum of the components of space extending from countless particles of matter. |

**Fig. 6.5** *The common properties of gravity and space*

the explanation for gravity which evolves from the unfolding logic in the vortex hypothesis.

In the vortex hypothesis, gravity is treated as a property of space and gravity has a lot in common with space when space is treated as discontinuous. Gravity acts and space extends in three dimensions from the centre of each particle of matter over an unlimited range. Both gravity and space are responsible for the apparent curvature of light and just as the space extending from a body is the addition of every space quantum from the body, so the gravity of a body is the sum of the components of gravity acting from every particle within it. To this extent, the vortex hypothesis supports Einstein's thinking that gravity is more an effect of space than the mediation of an arbitrary force field.

However, in the vortex hypothesis, whilst space and gravity are treated as one and the same thing - vortex energy - like charge, gravity is treated as a manifestation of the intrinsically dynamic nature of matter and space. Because of the similarity between the equations for charge and gravity, I like to think of gravity as a weak vortex interaction - an interaction which causes vortices to centralise on one another. But if it is a vortex interaction, why is it so much weaker than other vortex interactions such as charge and magnetism? Does it have a polar opposite such as a force of levity? Why is it only attractive? These questions are answered in the cosmology of the vortex.

Chapter 7

# COSMOLOGY
# OF THE
# VORTEX

*"Let us hope that out of this chaotic riddle will come a profound and simplifying answer. We may be likened to those who knew only Ptolemy's complex description of the solar system. What we need is a Copernicus to assimilate and interpret the data with a generalisation which will not only solve the riddle, but lift our sights to levels we cannot now foresee."*

*Richards, Sears, Wehr & Zemansky*

The cosmology of the vortex can be portrayed in an imaginary journey through the Alician dimension - the dimension of size. In your mind's eye, visualise the centre of the proton expanding as a minute bubble into a sphere of energy. As it expands, it grows to make way for another bubble growing out of the proton centre. New bubbles of energy keep popping out of that minute point to create the steady stream of concentric spheres that form the proton. Now imagine yourself travelling with one of the bubbles as it goes on its journey through the Universe.

You are now out of the nucleus. Expanding like a balloon, the space extending from your proton becomes too thin to perceive, but the spheres of energy expanding out of all the other particles in the nucleus merge with it to form a sphere which you can perceive. This sphere of energy grows out from the nucleus just as your original sphere grew out of the proton. There are larger spheres ahead of you and smaller spheres behind, all expanding on the same journey. As your bubble of energy expands out into the atom, you see concentric spheres of energy travelling in the opposite direction. They are shrinking into the electrons orbiting the nucleus.

You are now surrounded by millions of atoms in a DNA molecule as your sphere grows to envelop the nucleus of the cell. It contains the energy expanding out of all the atoms in that nucleus. Swelling past mitochondria factories, busy membranes and engorged vacuoles, you find yourself outside a brain cell travelling with the vortex energy expanding out of the entire cell. Still growing, the sphere of energy is as big as your brain, then your body. It is now no longer a sphere but is an extension of the shape of your body. There are other humans milling about and your own aura of energy merges with theirs as it continues to grow. First they shrink to the size of ants and then they vanish. Woods and meadows are beneath you, then they diminish to a chequered counterpane and you can discern your own country under broken cloud.

Now you are with a vast bubble of energy which grows to enclose the entire Earth. The sphere is 13 thousand kilometres in diameter and contains vortex energy from every proton in the planet. Again there are spheres expanding in front of you and more coming up behind. Your view is that of an astronaut looking back on Earth but your experience would be no different from rising out and away from the atomic nucleus or the nucleus of your brain cell - it is all relative.

To begin with, the Earth is vast beneath you, but then as your sphere of energy continues to expand, the planet seems to shrink. One moment she is the terrestrial globe, then sparkling for an instant like a sapphire suspended in space, she is gone. You are with a sphere of vortex energy 12 million kilometres in diameter which surrounds the entire solar system. Jupiter looks just like a gemstone and the Sun an orb of gold, as your bubble grows to envelop the three stars of Alpha Centuri, then the dancing duo of Sirius and Barnards single star. It is then 100 trillion kilometres in diameter and still growing.

At a million, trillion kilometres in diameter your bubble becomes a mighty disc-shaped spheroid surrounding the entire Milky Way galaxy. As a single bubble, it contains vortex energy from every proton in all the billions of stars, planets and dust clouds that our galaxy contains. Soon you are looking down on a distant crown of a hundred billion gems and your bubble of energy has grown to encompass a cluster of some twenty galaxies including the Milky Way, the Magellanic clouds and the fabulous Andromeda, bursting with billions of stars. The cluster shrinks from sight as your bubble grows to enclose hundreds of galaxy clusters far, far larger than our own local group. Mighty Virgo with her thousand galaxies and Canes Venatici with thousands more. Expanding out beyond this super-cluster, your bubble is now a billion, trillion kilometres in diameter but things are no different than when you were riding astride the atomic bubble. Everything is simply on a different scale. At 100 billion, trillion kilometres your bubble has swallowed the tremendous super-clusters, Perseus, Hercules and Indus. At 200 billion, trillion kilometres you are riding on energy from thousands of super-clusters. At 300 billion, trillion kilometres you begin to encounter the mysterious quasars radiating hundreds of times as much energy as a star. At 400 billion, trillion kilometres your bubble sweeps up countless millions of quasars and with a diameter of 500 billion, trillion kilometres it becomes the largest sphere of space; the outermost frontier of the Universe of matter.

You have come to the outermost limit of space because your gargantuan sphere has stopped expanding and is beginning to shrink. Whereas before you were travelling with the drifting galaxies now you are moving against them. Faint specks of light grow into mighty super-clusters. It is Perseus, Hercules and Indus that rush up to meet you, growing at a terrifying rate, and then fly past. You are still travelling forward but your sphere seems to be shrinking back the way it came as Virgo appears out of a distant sparkle and expands into a thousand galaxies. Racing down toward swirling maelstroms of light, glittering red, gold and blue like jewelled crowns, you just catch sight of Andromeda as you are enveloped once again by the Milky Way. Single points of light grow toward you. First there is Barnards star, then you see the Sun growing bigger and bigger. You can now discern Jupiter, Mars and Saturn, but you are zooming down toward a beautiful white and blue marbled globe as she swells up to meet you. You can see Europe and Asia, Africa, Australasia and the Americas amidst the shifting cloud patterns, but it is to your own country that you are irresistibly drawn. The same cities, towns and patchwork landscape. You are now streaking toward a human body. At first it is a distant speck, no bigger than a mite, but as your sphere shrinks towards its surface you recognise it as your own body but it grows bigger than a giant. Hair is standing like a forest and, shooting past bacteria on your scalp - busy at their business of feeding, growing and reproducing - you pass into your head to be enveloped by a single brain cell. Then sweeping down past mitochondria and membranes, you arrive in the nucleus. A DNA coil grows up toward you as you hurtle down into a double helix strand and then into an atom which swallows you whole. Spheres of energy are expanding out of its orbiting vortices. But they aren't electrons, they are positrons! You have just passed through a world of anti-matter and you are drawing ever closer to the anti-matter atomic nucleus. Finally you are sucked down into an anti-proton and with your sphere of energy you collapse into the single point of its centre. From this point of *singularity* your sphere of vortex energy grows again, up and out, to form a proton and you find yourself back, right where you started from.

The cosmology of the vortex, portrayed in this imaginary journey, comes from resolving an obvious problem with the vortex. Where is all the energy in the vortex coming from? The vortex can only exist if the concentric spheres of energy are continually growing or shrinking through it. It would seem that the centre of each vortex is an infinite source, or sink, of energy. The same problem, which applies in the smallest realms of space - in the heart of each vortex - would apply in the largest realm of space which encompasses all the galaxies in the Universe. This, the largest sphere of space, would have vortex energy from every particle in existence passing through it. Again, where would all the vortex energy go? This would also appear to be an infinite sink and source of energy. An answer to these questions, in keeping with the Law that *energy is neither created nor destroyed*, comes from observing nature.

In nature, things flow endlessly only when they are part of a cycle. Consider a whirlpool in a river. The whirlpool exists because water is continually flowing through it. There is an endless flow of water in the river because the river is part of the water cycle with numerous springs at one end and a single ocean at the other. The water cycle is divided into two halves. One half is the flow of water from the springs to the ocean through the rivers. The other half is the flow from the ocean to the springs through the rain.

The unending flow of energy in the vortex could be accounted for through a universal cycle of vortex energy, which would appear to have a lot in common with the water cycle. Energy flows through the vortex as in a river, from the innumerable centres of sub-atomic particles - like springs - to the largest sphere of space - the ocean.

Because we humans are formed out of the vortices of energy in matter, like fish in a river, we would be aware of only one half of the cycle of vortex energy. Fish, immersed in the waters of rivers, know only the river. They have no knowledge of clouds and rain. This is the *fish dilemma*. However, drops of rain falling into the surface of the river would show another form of water existing beyond the river which could lead to an account for the water cycle and explain the endless flow of water in the river.

Like drops of rain penetrating the surface of the river, particles of anti-matter penetrating the world of matter suggest a universal cycle of vortex energy.

The observed world of matter may be but half of the Universe. There could be another half formed out of anti-matter. Through these two halves of the Universe, vortex energy could flow in an endless cycle and between these two halves, connected in a circle, space would be infinite.

The vortex could be pictured as a funnel. The centre of the vortex, representing the smallest point of space, could be described as zero-space and represented by the small end of the funnel. Energy would spiral in to form the funnel representing a negatively charged particle of matter. Then, passing through the zero-space point as though it were a tunnel, it would spiral out to form an identical vortex funnel - representing a positively charged particle of anti-matter.

This picture suggests that every vortex in the world of matter would share a common centre with an identical vortex in the world of anti-matter. The anti-matter vortex would have the same mass as the vortex of matter but it would be flowing in the opposite direction. The two vortices would be connected like Siamese twins so they could be described as *Siamese twin particles*.

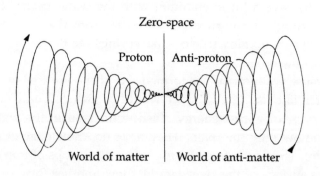

**Fig. 7.1** *Vortices of matter and anti-matter*

Every electron in our world of matter would share a common zero-space point with a positron in the world of anti-matter. Vortex energy would flow into the electron to form a negative charge, through the centre and out of the positron to form a positive charge. Because of their common centre, these particles would be inseparable. The same would apply to protons. Every proton would be connected through its centre to an anti-proton. Vortex energy would flow into the anti-proton to form a negative charge, through the zero-space point and out through the proton to form a positive charge. The proton and anti-proton would also be Siamese twin particles. The idea that there is an anti-matter half to the Universe is supported by the *mirror-symmetry* of matter and anti-matter. Practically every particle of matter has a twin, a mirror-symmetrical anti-particle.

If every particle of matter is connected to a particle of anti-matter then every form and action in our world must be mirrored in the world of anti-matter. Actions could only be mirrored if

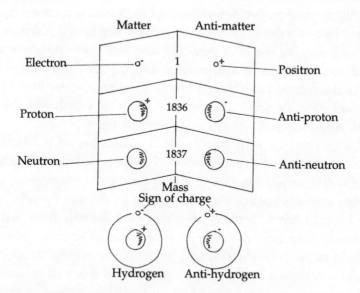

***Fig. 7.2** The mirror symmetry of matter and anti-matter*

every quantum entity in our world were shadowed by a quantum entity in the world of anti-matter. Symmetry would therefore demand that every photon in the world of matter must have a shadow photon in the world of anti-matter.

The existence of shadow photons explains how particles and anti-particles can move apart in pair-particle production. In Carl Anderson's original experiment, a gamma ray photon entered a proton in the nucleus of a lead atom and was transformed into an electron and positron pair of particles. Symmetry demands that at the same time the shadow gamma ray photon would have entered an anti-proton in the anti-matter lead atom, to be transformed into a duplicate pair. The natural electron in our world would have been Siamese twinned with the natural positron in the anti-matter world, and the unnatural positron in our world would have been backed with an unnatural electron in the world of anti-matter. What occurred, in effect, was that one of the Siamese pairs inverted to show an anti-particle in each world. As Carl Anderson observed the first positron ever seen on Earth, the anti-matter version of Carl Anderson was observing the first electron ever to be seen on anti-matter Earth. Considering himself and his world of positrons and anti-protons to be matter and our world to be anti-matter, anti-matter Anderson would have discovered what he considered to be anti-matter in the same instant as Anderson. The question remains, which was the real Carl Anderson and which was a mere reflection?

The vortex cosmology leads to a number of predictions. Matter is attracted to anti-matter. Therefore, particles of matter in our world would experience a pull through the regions of zero-space towards particles of anti-matter in the other world. The pull would not be between the connected Siamese-twin particles because they belong to the same system of energy. The pull would occur between different vortex pairs. Acting through the regions occupied by the centres of particles, this pull would be a centralising force that would cause particles to conglomerate in both worlds. The pull would be weak compared with other forces in our world because it comes from another world that is remote from us. This centralising pull on matter would be, in effect, a contraction of space quanta and would be effective as an acceleration.

It is this vortex interaction between matter and anti-matter, acting through the heart of matter, that could provide a force-field account for gravity. Being a radial interaction between vortices, it could also be explained in terms of relative accelerations, and so would fulfil the requirements of the principle of equivalence of forces that gravity be explained in terms of both, rather than either, interacting force fields or relative accelerations.

To complete the cycle of vortex energy, the worlds of matter and anti-matter must share the same largest sphere of space through which vortex energy from both worlds would continually flow. In the vortex cosmology, the infinity of space is a circle in which the worlds of matter and anti-matter are connected in the smallest and largest realms of space. Infinite space could also be represented by the infinity figure of eight. Each connecting loop would represent the separate halves of the Universe through which vortex energy continually cycles.

In the vortex cosmology there is a polar opposite to gravity. This is a pull on matter from the world of anti-matter through the largest sphere of space. Acting through the largest sphere of space, it affects the largest bodies of matter. It would cause the decentralisation of matter because it comes from the outermost reaches of the Universe. The pull would therefore cause galaxies to fly apart from one another, which would appear as an expansion of the Universe.

At present, it is widely believed that the Universe is expanding because of a push on matter, caused by a *big bang* at the beginning of time. However, in the vortex cosmology the expansion is considered to be only apparent, and because it is caused by a pull rather than a push, it presents an antithesis to the big bang theory. The arrival of an antithesis throws a thesis into question, so it is possible that the Universe didn't begin with a big bang.  Alternatively, a synthesis may be found between the big bang theory and the vortex cosmology.

Certainly a new explanation for the evidence that galaxies are flying apart, provides yet another example of why no experiment or observation can ever be taken as certain proof of a particular theory.  Another example of this is the $3^0K$ microwave radiation which permeates the whole of space.  This is taken as conclusive evidence of the big bang.  However, in his book, *The Intelligent Universe*, Sir Fred Hoyle suggests that this background radiation in space could be taken as evidence to support his theory that the Universe is full of carbon based life.

As it stands, the big bang theory has certain innate weaknesses.  To begin with, it is clear from the theory that in the beginning matter and anti-matter must have existed in equal proportions.  In order to explain the apparent absence of anti-matter in the Universe now, the theory makes the arbitrary assumption that there must have been slightly more matter than anti-matter to begin with.  Most of the matter must have annihilated with all of the anti-matter and the residual matter is what we perceive as the Universe today.  There are no grounds for this speculation.  Lord Rutherford's Law of Conservation of Charge requires that anti-matter must have been created in exactly equal proportions to matter in the birth of the Universe.  In the vortex cosmology an account is provided for anti-matter and this is used to explain gravity and why distant galaxies are accelerating toward the outermost reaches of space; which brings me to another weakness in the big bang theory.  Why do more distant galaxies accelerate away from us faster than galaxies that are close to us?  If the Universe started with an explosion the outermost galaxies would be more likely to slow down rather than speed up, because objects either maintain or lose their momentum as they fly out from the centre of an explosion.  They would only gain momentum if an additional force were to act upon them.  In the vortex cosmology, the pull from anti-matter suggests a force that would cause the galaxies to accelerate.

If a galaxy of matter were to accelerate toward a galaxy of anti-matter, and vice versa, eventually they would meet and annihilate. If the cosmology of the vortex is correct there should be some evidence of annihilation going on at the outermost reaches of the Universe. In fact, the furthermost things from us are quasars, and quasars are bodies which radiate about two hundred times the energy of normal stars. Since stars produce energy through nuclear fusion, which consumes just over 0.5% of their total proton mass, a process which produces 200 times this radiation of energy would obviously be consuming 100% of the mass of a proton. Just such a process is the annihilation of matter and anti-matter.

It is at the two 'ends of the Alician dimension', where matter and anti-matter meet, that annihilation would most likely occur, so quasars should also be observed in the regions of greatest centralisation of space as well as in the regions where space is most decentralised. In fact, quasars also occur in the central regions of many galaxies - regions where matter is very centralised.

As stars exhaust their nuclear fuel and cool down, they eventually collapse in on themselves due to gravity. First they form a *red giant* then a *white dwarf* star. In the demise of very massive stars, gravity can be sufficiently strong for a *black hole* to form. Some astronomers believe that the centre of a galaxy is an enormous black-hole engulfing millions of exhausted stars. The black hole represents the greatest density of matter possible and, as it forms, an anti-matter black hole would be forming 'inside' it, or rather on the other side of it, through the smallest realms of space. Here, where particles of matter are centralised into the smallest volume, they would be converging on the anti-matter. Annihilation between the matter and anti-matter would occur. To begin with, the energy released by this process could not radiate from the black hole because it would be acting like a gargantuan 'proton' vortex, capturing the energy of annihilation in its spiral space-path. However, with annihilation, the mass of the black hole would shrink and its gravity would diminish. Its ability to hold onto captured energy would be decreasing all the time. Due to progressive annihilation the energy contained by the black hole would be rapidly increasing. Eventually there would have to be a crossover point between the diminishing gravity and the increasing release of energy from annihilation. This would be a threshold point where energy would begin to escape and radiate away - then the formation would cease to be a black hole and would become a quasar. If this is correct then a black-hole would be only a temporary astronomical formation, occurring as a step in the transition of star into a quasar, one of the most brilliant lights in the Universe. In the cosmology of the vortex the black hole appears, not as an astral grave, but as a stellar pupa, holding the metamorphosis of the 'caterpillar' star into the quasar 'butterfly'.

In the vortex hypothesis, gravitational energy is treated as energy of annihilation between matter and anti-matter - which fits with Einstein's belief that gravitational energy is derived from the destruction of mass. When a body falls, due to gravity, it releases energy on impact. This energy is derived from the destruction of mass because a moving body has a greater mass than a body at rest. As the body falls in the world of matter, a mirror-image body of anti-matter would also be falling, so both would make their impact and release of energy simultaneously. There would be an equal annihilation of mass in the matter and anti-matter as both bodies come to rest and at rest they would be closer to their ultimate, complete annihilation. In order to lift the bodies again, work would have to be done which would require an equal input of energy to that released when they came to rest. As the bodies accelerate against gravity, due to this work, their mass would increase proportionately.

The fall of every bit of matter on Earth is another step in the inexorable progress toward annihilation. As you pick up an object that has fallen, you use up energy from the Sun which was acting to keep the particles in the Sun from falling together due to gravity. Eventually, when the Sun's reserves of fuel are exhausted, the inertia of gravity will take over and all the matter within it will collapse toward anti-matter and annihilation. Even though the Sun is too small to form a black hole, and will eventually settle down to being a white dwarf, this could be swallowed up by neighbouring black holes as the whole galaxy consumes its reserves of nuclear fuel and collapses under the influence of gravity.

Annihilation is the ultimate, complete transformation of matter into light. It represents the end of the vortex as it is transformed into the wave form of energy. How the vortex comes into being and how vortices separate out into the two halves of the vortex cycle is an unanswered question. Perhaps, in the quasar, from the vast amounts of annihilation energy, new vortex particles are formed to replace the old ones that are annihilated. If this were so then the process would be one of transformation and regeneration rather than ultimate vortex annihilation. Then the quasar could represent the early stage in the life of the new galaxy as well as the final stage in the life of the old galaxy in the way that birth is on the other side of the door of death. This is only speculation and, whatever the situation, there is no reason to suppose that the energy - the movement underlying the vortex - was ever created or that it will ever be destroyed. Energy exists. All we ever observe are its unending transformations.

This completes the vortex model for the physical Universe. It is presented as a new picture, a new way of applying the paints of observation onto the canvas of understanding. But can it ever become a good theory? In *A Brief History of Time*, Stephen Hawking stipulated that: "A theory is a good theory if it satisfies two requirements: it must accurately describe a large class of observations on the basis of a model that contains only a few arbitrary elements, and it must make definite predictions about the results of future observations."

The vortex hypothesis could be a good theory because it offers a complete picture of the Universe from the single arbitrary assumption that ***sub-atomic particles of matter are vortices of energy.*** (A principle known as *Ockham's razor* can be invoked in favour of the vortex hypothesis. The 14th Century philosopher William of Ockham used the Law of Economy in ideas with such sharpness that it came to be known as Ockham's razor. Stating: *non sunt multiplicanda entia praeter necessitatem*, i.e. entities are not to be multiplied beyond necessity, Ockham argued for accepting the thesis which employs the least number of assumptions. The Law of Economy in ideas was also invoked by Galileo, in defending the simplest hypothesis of the heavens. It has been employed by numerous scientists since then.)

The vortex hypothesis is also relatively simple, clear and understandable to anyone of reasonable intelligence - which I believe is also the sign of a good theory. It remains only for me to make some testable predictions.

The textbook, *Modern University Physics*, concluded with the statement: "What we need is...to assimilate and interpret the data with a generalisation which will not only solve the riddle, but lift our sights to levels we cannot now foresee."

The generalisation I have presented offers a new way to assimilate and interpret the data in order to solve the riddle of modern physics. It then lifts our sights to levels we cannot now foresee within science, in the predictions that I make to test it.

These predictions are based on the symmetry 'as above, so below: as below, so above'. I suggest that patterns observed in the atom should apply to the Universe as a whole.

In the atom, electrons are observed to occur in distinct energy levels or quantum states. They are also observed to take a 'quantum leap' from one state to another. As they cannot exist between the quantum levels, in the quantum leap electrons vanish from one quantum level in the atom and appear on another.

My first prediction is that the physical Universe is but one level of energy in an ascending series of quantum realities and that the laws of physics are much the same from one level to the next. The difference between the levels is the intrinsic speed of the energy that forms them. Each level is a discrete quantum state formed out of energy with a critical speed of movement. There could be energy levels above and below us. I describe the energy states above us as worlds of *super-energy*. This prediction could be tested by drawing super-energy into our world, from the higher quantum realities, in ways that cannot be accounted for in terms of normal physical or chemical reactions.

My second prediction is that bodies could ascend the series by undergoing a quantum leap from one energy state in the Universe to another. In effect they would vanish out of our world and appear in another or vice versa. This prediction can be tested by observing the appearance and disappearance of bodies of matter in ways that cannot be explained by normal physical, chemical or biological processes.

The study of paranormal and extra-terrestrial phenomena offer one way of testing this prediction. This is the subject of *The Vortex: Key to Future Science*. The rumours of imminent human and planetary ascension offer another way of testing this prediction.

Chapter 8

# SUPER-ENERGY RESEARCH

*"We can't find anything wrong with it so we will just have to ignore it."*

*Robert Oppenheimer*

Predictions are only meaningful to science if they can be tested. The prediction of super-energy - energy existing beyond the speed of light - could be tested by the appearance of inexplicable power in our world, that is power coming into the physical part of the Universe from the realms of super-energy, in apparent contravention of the Laws of Thermodynamics.

According to the Laws of Thermodynamics, energy can neither be created nor destroyed and the total energy in a closed system is always constant. If it could be shown that energy has appeared, apparently out of nowhere, then it would have to be accepted that either the Laws of Thermodynamics are invalid or the physical Universe is not a closed system but is part of a greater system of energy. The Laws of Thermodynamics apply to the Universe as a whole and, within that whole, the transfer of energy between systems, on different levels of reality, should be possible. The appearance of unaccounted energy in a physical system could show a discrepancy, not in the Laws of Thermodynamics, but in the existing, outmoded, scientific paradigm which does not allow for the existence of any realities apart from the observed physical reality. Because of prejudice in science against non-physical realities, circumstantial evidence is ignored, dismissed or discredited in the public mind by means of fraud.

The appearance of *crop circles* is a case in point. They are created by inexplicable powers but because they cannot be dismissed or ignored they have been discredited, in the public mind, by the production of fraudulent circles. No effort has been made by the scientific establishment to distinguish true from false formations, and efforts by individual scientists to show evidence that most crop circles could not be produced by hoaxers have been ignored. The fraud has been fully supported by the media in a deliberate attempt to suppress evidence of this paranormal phenomenon.

At a lecture to the Society for Psychical Research, the neurochemist Diana Clift commented: "I remember reading in both the *Guardian* and the *Independent* newspapers that self-confessed hoaxers Doug Bower and Dave Chorley were responsible for most of the 5,000 circles which appeared in England for the last ten years.

"Here we have the extraordinary spectacle of these two hoaxers leaving the pub at closing time and averaging five circles a night for every night of the growing season over ten years!"

In the video of Richard Hoagland's lecture at the United Nations, *The Terrestrial Connection*, Hoagland points out that the tetrahedral geometry in some of the circles is far too precise to be the work of hoaxers trampling the corn with ropes and boards. He argued that the formations in the crops offer supportive evidence for the existence of extra-terrestrial intelligence, perhaps of non-physical origin. Hoagland also cited evidence for the appearance of inexplicable energy in the Universe. He said that the Sun is producing fewer particle emissions than would be expected if all of its energy were thermo-nuclear in origin, suggesting that stars could contain "...interdimensional doorways accessing multi-dimensional energy". He then cited the research of Bruce de Palma showing diagrams of apparatus which de

Palma was using to access multi-dimensional energy, in apparent contravention of the known laws of physics.

Bruce de Palma used rotating magnetic discs to access super-energy. He is just one of a number of individuals involved in a field of extraordinary research that seems to have been passed unnoticed by most mainstream scientists. This research into super-energy generators, usually based on rotational motion of some kind, has generally been the domain of inventors, with modest facilities and amateur engineering skills, working outside of university and industrial scientific establishments. These extraordinary research projects and the discoveries stemming from them are highly controversial, but they provide supportive evidence which serves to vindicate the vortex predictions and, at the same time, the science of the vortex provides a framework of understanding which makes many of these controversial discoveries theoretically plausible.

John Searl was an electrical engineer, employed by the Midland Electricity Board, when he constructed an arrangement of spinning discs to generate and spin an electro-magnetic field. His apparatus consisted of a segmented rotor disc which was set spinning at great speed through electro-magnets at its periphery. The electro-magnets, energised from the rotor, were intended to boost the electro-motive force. The generator, about three feet in diameter, was first tested in the open, by Searl and a friend, in 1952. To begin with, it produced the expected electric power but an unexpectedly high voltage. This quickly exceeded a million volts producing a crackling sound and the smell of ozone. In Searl's own words: "Once the machine had passed a certain threshold of potential, the energy output exceeded the input. From then on the energy output seemed to be virtually limitless."

Then something really spectacular happened. As the generator continued to increase in potential, it lifted off the ground and broke free of its mountings and the engine. It floated in the air, all the time spinning faster and faster. The air around it glowed pink with ionisation and nearby radio receivers were switched on spontaneously due to electro-magnetic induction. Then the apparatus accelerated off into space and was never seen again!

In subsequent experiments Searl mounted his generators, which he built up to thirty feet in diameter, more firmly in the ground. But they still tore themselves free of the Earth, taking the foundations with them. They appeared to produce a powerful anti-gravity force and from the hemispherical crater left in the ground, it was deduced that this force was operating over a sphere with the generator at its centre.

Searl had stumbled across extraordinary phenomena associated with rotational motion. He was one of a number of inventors who discovered a means of generating boundless free energy and an anti-gravity force simply by setting up vortex systems.

The research began in the 19th century, when Michael Faraday made some remarkable but little known discoveries in regard to spinning magnets. These have been developed by a number of 20th century inventors, including Bruce de Palma and Adam Trombly, into *N-machines* or *Uni-polar generators*. Faraday's discovery was remarkably simple but totally revolutionary. If a bar magnet is set spinning, the differential in velocity, down the radius of each turning magnetic element, sets up a magnetic vortex. This effect is more pronounced with a series of bar magnets radiating from a central spinning hub or a spinning magnetic disc. At a certain threshold of angular velocity, the magnetic vortex sets up an inter-dimensional energy portal. This simple arrangement is the operating principle of many highly efficient, lightweight super-energy generators. For example, World Harmony (International) of Western Australia are aware of a super-energy turbine that is only twenty inches in diameter, five inches in height and twenty pounds in weight which is producing approximately 1.5 megawatts of electrical power (sufficient to provide electricity to 500 homes). It is also reported to have lifted several tons of weight.

The free energy and anti-gravity properties of vortex motion were discovered quite independently by the Austrian inventor, Victor Schauberger. Victor Schauberger, famous for his construction of logging flumes, was known as the 'wizard of water'. He set icy water into spin and from this form of vortex motion he constructed a super-energy, anti-gravity turbine.

Victor Schauberger was a young ranger in the wilderness forest of Bernerau, in Austria, when he made his first observations of the power in vortex motion. In his own words, from *Living Water*: "It was spawning time one early spring moonlight night. I was sitting by a waterfall waiting to catch a fish poacher. What then occurred took place so quickly that I was hardly able to comprehend. In the moonlight falling directly onto the crystal-clear water, every movement of the fish, gathered in large numbers, could be observed. Suddenly the trout dispersed due to the appearance of a particularly large fish which swam up from below to confront the waterfall. It seemed as if it wished to disturb the other trout and danced in great twisting movements in the undulating water as it swam quickly to and fro. Then as suddenly the large trout disappeared in the jet of the waterfall which glistened like falling metal. I saw it fleetingly under a conically shaped stream of water, dancing in a wild spinning movement the reason for which was not at first clear to me. It then came out of this spinning movement and floated motionlessly upwards. On reaching the lower curve of the waterfall it tumbled over and with a strong push reached behind the upper curve of the waterfall."

"Deep in thought I filled my pipe and as I wended my way homewards, smoked it to the end. I often subsequently saw the same sequence of play of a trout jumping a high waterfall."

Schauberger observed that the vortex motion of water, a little above freezing, seemed to lift the trout up the waterfall. He was also intrigued by the way trout, in the mountain streams, would remain motionless, as if suspended, in the fast flowing water, then dart like lightning upstream. Schauberger was convinced that the turbulence and vortex motion of water, at its greatest density, generated a force in the opposite direction to the flow of the stream. He believed that trout could seek out the upstream flow of energy and use it to remain motionlessly suspended in the fast flow of water or to propel them upstream and over waterfalls. He believed that trout also employed a force generated by the spiral motion of water passing from its gills over the surface of its body.

Victor Schauberger was convinced that the conical vortex or cycloid spiral was a source of energy. To test his idea he set himself the task of building a vortex turbine based on the same principle of twisting, reeling and spinning that he had observed in the fast flowing waters of freezing mountain streams. His most successful designs were based on the corkscrew-shaped spirals expelled from the gills of trout so he called his apparatus the *trout turbine*.

In all his experiments Schauberger found that the temperature and structure of the water was critical as was the shape of his turbine and the materials out of which it was constructed. In the early 1930's he fabricated conical pipes of special materials which contained a corkscrew turbine. Operated by an electric motor, the spiral turbines screwed water into a vortex flow and directed the water onto a conventional water turbine coupled to a generator.

Schauberger claimed that as the water was screwed faster and faster, it suddenly began to produce enormous amounts of energy. Coupled to a dynamo, the turbine began to generate more electricity than the input motor was consuming. The system quickly went out of control as the apparatus tore itself away from its holdings and smashed itself against the ceiling. When Schauberger experimented with air turbines he found the same thing happened. Regardless of the medium, vortex motion seemed to generate energy, apparently out of nowhere, and it also produced a powerful anti-gravity force.

Just before the outbreak of the Second World War a Vienna firm called Kertl were ordered by Adolf Hitler to construct and test Schauberger's vortex turbines with a view to using them in aircraft engines. An engineer called Aloys Kokaly was employed in the manufacture of certain parts. On one occasion when he delivered the parts to the Kertl factory he was told, "This must be prepared for Mr Schauberger on orders from higher authority, but when it's finished, it's going out onto the street, because on an earlier test on one of these strange contraptions, it went right through the roof of the factory."

An American inventor, Joseph Newman found that free energy could be obtained by setting electro-magnetic fields spinning. Newman's machine consisted of a number of rotating magnets wound with copper wire to form a reciprocating magnetic armature. According to Newman, as the armature was set spinning, an electromagnetic force was induced and set into a spiral pattern of motion around the current-carrying copper wire.

Like the other generators, Newman's apparatus appeared to produce energy out of nowhere. On March 21, 1986, *The Guardian* reported that Dr Roger Hastings, chief physicist for the Sperry-Univac Corporation, tested Newman's apparatus. He found that the production efficiency of the machine was far greater than 100%. On September 20th 1985 Hastings issued an affidavit to the effect that, "...On September 19th 1985 the motor was operated at 1,000 and 2,000 volts battery input, with output powers of 50 and 100 watts respectively. Input power in these tests were 7 and 14 watts yielding efficiencies of 700% and 1,400% respectively..."

De Palma, Trombly, Searl, Schauberger and Newman, working independently, all discovered free energy in apparent defiance of the Laws of Thermodynamics. The free-energy machines they constructed are called *over-unity* machines because they operated in excess of 100% efficiency. Their experiments have not been taken seriously by professional scientists on the grounds that it is impossible to get energy out of nowhere. These, and other super-energy researchers have either been opposed, ignored or labelled as pseudoscientists and cranks, and their apparatus has been dismissed as perpetual motion machines.

In 1987 Newman had his generator operating as the engine of
a car built on a Porsche chassis. Started by a battery the car ran
without any input of fuel. However, the American Patent Office
refused to grant him a patent for his invention on the grounds
that it was, to all intent and purpose, a perpetual motion machine.
On the basis that perpetual motion is impossible, alleged
inventions of perpetual motion machines are refused patents,
consequently the commercial development of his engine was
effectively blocked.

When Trombly attempted to patent his uni-polar generator he
was turned down by the U.S. Patent Office on similar grounds.
Nonetheless, the U.S. Defence authorities took out a court order
against him and threatened him with 10-year imprisonment for
infringing secret government research into uni-polar generators.

Schauberger thought he had discovered a means of 'cold
nuclear fusion'. He described his vortex turbines as *implosion
devices*. However, his research was discouraged by the Allies.
Shortly after the end of World War II a group of American
military personnel arrived at Schauberger's home in Vienna,
seized his apparatus and took him into protective custody. What
they left behind was then destroyed by agents who blew up his
apartment. The American authorities forbade him to resume his
research under threat of re-arrest.[6]

The British authorities treated Searl in similar fashion. In
1982, whilst he was in the middle of an experiment at his home in
Mortimer, Berkshire, England, a group of officials entered the
house and confiscated his apparatus. On the basis that he was
using electricity without paying bills, he was charged with
stealing electricity and fined. The court would not accept that he
was generating his own power through a free-energy device. His
apparatus was never returned so he refused to pay the fine and
was then sent to prison for contempt of court. Whilst in detention
a fire broke out at his house, destroying most of his records.

Another electrical engineer to receive similar treatment, in
response to his pioneering work, was the Austrian scientist, Dr.

Wilhelm Reich. Reich had emigrated to America where he attempted to develop his discovery of a means of tapping super-energy, which he described as *orgone energy*. He was able to use his orgone energy devices to dissipate storms and treat diseases, such as cancer. Because of this latter discovery he fell foul of the American Medical Association and Food and Drug Administration. He was also committed to prison for contempt of court. His books and records were then burnt and his research equipment was destroyed by the American authorities. Even though he was proclaimed as a quack and thoroughly discredited, Reich's discoveries were employed in secret research programmes and he was encouraged to continue his anti-gravity research whilst in prison.

In Germany it was the commercial backer rather than the inventor who was arrested. According to a report in *Deutsche Physik*, on May 19th 1992, at 8 a.m., six armed policemen burst into the home of Jurgen Sievers, the Director and General Deputy of a German Company called Becocraft. The house was searched and all papers linked to the company were confiscated. On the 15th of June Sievers was arrested in the street and held in remand at Köln-Ossendorf. The criminal charge against Sievers and his company was investment fraud in respect to the commercial development of a free-energy device, invented by the Austrian inventor, Stephan Marinov.

It has always been difficult for people involved in the research and development of super-energy generators to defend themselves in court against a charge of fraud, because science does not allow for the existence of energy outside of the known, physical Universe. Science is supposed to be impartial yet, as far as I am aware, there has never been an impartial investigation into super-energy as a potential source of power, even in view of the energy crisis. This is understandable because the research flies in the face of current scientific thinking. However, I believe there is another reason why the development has been blocked.

In his book *Robots' Rebellion* David Icke speaks of an

international cohort - including top bankers and industrialists - with enormous economic power, which influences the decisions of governments and has society dancing to its tune, like a puppet on strings. Reports to support this *conspiracy theory* are controversial, nonetheless they abound and are taken very seriously by many people. I am certain that those who control funding have an influence over what is taught and researched in universities. It is also my belief that virtually unlimited funds have been made available for futile high-energy research, to keep physicists distracted from the truth which their paymasters prefer to keep secret.

I am not alone in the belief that there has been a deliberate effort to suppress super-energy technology. In their book, *The Philadelphia Experiment*, Brad Steiger and Alfred Bielek claim that a super-energy generator was operating, in a secret underground facility, in the United States of America during World War II. According to the agent, a decision was taken by higher powers to destroy the apparatus and develop nuclear energy instead

It is not difficult to appreciate why government and industry would want to block research into super-energy and choose nuclear energy instead - regardless of the hazards of radioactivity and pollution. The implications of super-energy, as a source of power, are staggering. Super-energy generators promise a more significant revolution in energy production than the discovery of fossil fuels and nuclear power. Fossil fuels and nuclear power are limited, non-renewable sources of energy which require a large capital investment. This maintains expensive energy production and therefore the generation of enormous income for those people who finance and control it. By contrast, super-energy technology offers an abundance of free energy - after the initial expense of purchasing a generator - and because of their innate simplicity and low production cost, the manufacture of generators could not be controlled. The entire population would have their own super-energy power plants which would negate the need for oil, gas, coal and nuclear power. If bankers, industrialists and governments were to sanction this development they would be cutting their own throats. Not only would they lose their investments in the power utilities, they would see the end of the transport industry. Super-energy, anti-gravity generators would cause existing forms of transport to become obsolete. With craft that float and run without gas, who would want to drive a car on the overcrowded roads or use a train or an aeroplane?

Because of this threat to the industrial and economic base of our society it would be naive to imagine that the prediction of super-energy, as a source of power, would ever be subjected to impartial tests in university or government laboratories. Perhaps this is just as well. If the prediction were to be vindicated, in the present moral climate super-energy technology would no doubt be deployed for military purposes. Given these circumstances, I treat the available evidence as sufficient to confirm the existence of super-energy. It is also my belief that the current scientific argument, that energy cannot exist beyond the speed of light, is just another myth in the doctrine of materialism which underlies the wholescale corruption that is destroying the Earth.

Chapter 9

# SUPER-ENERGY
# RESONANCE

*"A vital aspect of the enlightened state is the experience of an all-pervading unity."*

*Gary Zukav*

Modern physics may have established that particles cannot move faster than the speed of light, but this does not mean that movement is constrained to this speed. The speed of light is the upper limit of velocity if it is assumed that movement can only exist as the property of particles. However, this classical assumption of the atomic hypothesis is merely a reflection of outmoded materialism. If everything, including space-time, is formed out of particles of movement rather than particles in motion, then there is no reason why the speed of light should be the absolute limit to all speeds, as is commonly assumed today.

The concept of absolute parameters in the Universe was very much a part of classical thought. Mass, space, time and the laws of physics were thought to be absolute and invariable. However, with the turn of the 20th century it became clear that these classical assumptions were invalid. It was Einstein, of course, who showed that space and time, mass and the laws of physics were not absolute and invariable but were relative to the speed of light. Since then, most scientists have proclaimed that there is nothing absolute in the world of physics, but still, throughout the 20th century, the speed of light has been generally accepted as absolute and invariable - the ultimate frontier of the Universe.

When Einstein dismissed the concept of material substance he dismissed the *ether myth* which stemmed from it. (The idea of an ether came directly from the materialist idea that, 'before there can be motion there must be something that moves and space for it to move through'. When classical scientists realised that light consisted of waves, they couldn't conceive of wave motion without an underlying medium to support this motion. "How could you have waves without an ocean?" they argued, so they invented a hypothetical medium to support the waves of light, which they called the luminiferous ether.) Nonetheless, it would appear that the ether has been dismissed in name only because today many scientists talk about a 'sea of energy' underlying the wave-particles of matter and light. The concept of energy is no different from the ether idea if it treats energy as something underlying activity rather than activity itself. There is great resistance in the human mind to the idea that there could be movement without any underlying medium or material that moves, but this concept must be grasped if ever we are to understand the nature of energy, the fabric of the Universe.

Energy is simply a measure of activity or potential activity and treating it as something underlying activity, rather than the activity itself, has led to great confusion in physics. Richard Feynman knew this and he had the honesty to admit that most scientists have no idea what energy is. Nonetheless, I believe that an increasing number of physicists do understand the nature of energy. They have realised that there is nothing in the Universe apart from pure activity, movement and change, and have understood that energy is synonymous with this ceaseless motion. One such physicist is Fritjof Capra. Capra understood that there is no reality in the Universe apart from movement and activity when he wrote in *The Turning Point,*"...There is motion but there are, ultimately, no moving objects; there is activity but there are no actors; there are no dancers, there is only the dance."

Capra's description of particles, as 'particles of the dance rather than particles that are dancing,' is very clear and simple. His poetic statement embodies the new quantum hypothesis and conveys an obvious understanding of energy as pure, unsupported movement. To my mind, this understanding is the sign of a true quantum physicist.

Every movement has a speed, so if energy is movement, it must also have a speed. Because space, time, mass and energy are all relative to the speed of light, it would seem obvious that this must represent the speed of motion in energy as we perceive it. The energy which underlies everything in the physical part of the Universe must be movement at the speed of light.

If energy is nothing but movement at the speed of light, it is entirely possible that movements exist with speeds beyond that of light. I believe these movements constitute super-energy. If they do exist, it could not be within the confines of our space and time because physical space and time are relative to the speed of light. Neither could they occur within the bounds of our perceived reality, because we and our means of perception and scientific observation are formed out of movement at the speed of light. The study of energies beyond light would therefore appear to be beyond the scope of science. If, in the speed of light, we have established a limit to scientific observation, then the question is raised, 'what is the future for science?'

Science was founded on the principle that seeing is believing. This principle was important in its day because it dispelled the clouds of religious fear and superstition and led to an enormous expansion of knowledge through experiment and observation. However, the way we see things is coloured by our beliefs. Every system of belief is simply a different point of view and no experiment in science can show one point of view to be more true than another. I believe the early triumph of science was not in the overthrow of a set of religious doctrines in particular, but in the successful challenge to established beliefs in general. The problem, as I see it, is not what people believe but the way they limit themselves with their beliefs. Rigid beliefs cause closed minds, and science came in like a breath of fresh air to open people's minds to new possibilities, when religion was enclosing them in rigid dogmatism. Now science is established and it is presenting a new set of beliefs around which many human minds have closed. Most people close their minds and cling to a system of belief because of insecurity and fear of the unknown. This feature of the human mind is exhibited by the fundamentalist in religion and the sceptic in science. The die-hard sceptic, who will believe only in what he can see, portrays the psychological trait known as *flat-earth mentality*.

Most people in medieval Europe believed that the Earth was flat and the world ended at the horizon, and were constrained to Europe by this limiting belief. Before Christopher Columbus could set out to discover America, he had to conquer his fear of the unknown and break free of the flat-earth mentality. He had to have an open mind and allow for the possibility that the limits of his perception were not the limits to reality.

The speed of light is the limit to the world in which we live, but if we treat it as the absolute limit to reality, then, like those masses of unimaginative flat-earth thinkers, we will be stranded on the shores of our perceived reality. If there is energy beyond the speed of light, though it would exist beyond normal perception and scientific observation, it need not remain beyond the bounds of discovery and knowledge because there may be indirect ways of establishing its reality. However, we will never begin the process of its discovery unless we allow for the possibility of its existence. The process of discovery begins with the entertainment of a possibility - Columbus discovered America only because he entertained the possibility that the Earth was not flat, but was a globe on which the east could be reached by sailing west.

The first step in coming to terms with the idea of energy

beyond the speed of light is to redefine the term energy. In science, the word energy is strictly confined to physical reality constrained by the speed of light. However, the word energy is required to describe all movements in the Universe regardless of their intrinsic speeds. To overcome this difficulty, I describe the energy bounded by the speed of light and underlying physical reality, as *physical-energy* - to distinguish it from super-energy existing beyond the speed of light.

If the symmetry of 'as above, so below' is applied, then just as physical energy is divided into particles, super-energy would be divided into particles and these particles could also occur in the forms of waves and vortices. These could set up atoms, molecules and bodies much as physical energy creates the atoms, molecules and bodies of matter which make up our world. Then, as physical energy in each vortex sets up the space and time, so vortices of these higher energies could also set up space and time. They could establish other worlds, other domains of space and time quite distinct from our own, and these could be described as other quantum realities. I present these ideas not as an assumption but as a prediction.

The prediction of other quantum realities is in line with quantum thinking. Whereas in classical thinking it was believed that energy existed in a continuous band, which could be likened to a ramp, the great achievement of quantum theory has been to show that energy is discontinuous. The distribution of energy is more like a flight of steps than a ramp. For example, electrons in the atom can only exist within certain energy levels - none occur in between. Also particles of matter occur with specific mass-energies and none exist between these quantum steps.

The quantum steps of energy could be likened to different animals. If particles of matter are taken as an example, electrons could be likened to mice and protons to elephants. Each elephant or mouse is an individual particle of its own species and there is no limit to the number of individuals that can occur in the species. But there is a discontinuity between the species. Each

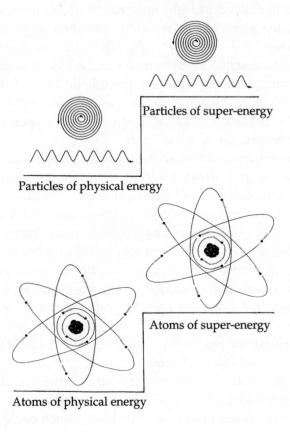

*Fig. 9.1* *Identical particles in physical energy and super-energy*

animal belongs to its own species and each species exists on its own step of the evolutionary ladder.

Just as no one knows why a proton happens to have a mass-energy 1836 times that of an electron, there is no immediate explanation for why the speed of light is critical to physical energy. All that can be said is that particles of motion, at the speed of light, form the quantum reality in which we live. As such, it could be said that the speed of light is the critical speed out of which our physical quantum reality - our world of activity

- is built, but the physical part of the Universe may be just one quantum step in the total Universe of energy. It would be the step on which all reality is relative to the speed of light. The other quantum realities - other worlds of activity - would be built out of different critical speeds of movement so that the Universe would consist of an ascending series of quantum steps, with the reality on each step being relative to a successively higher critical speed of motion.

The four dimensions of space and time are established by the forms of energy - such as the vortex - on each step and because space and time are an integral part of each quantum reality they could not occur between the steps. The ascending quantum realities could not, therefore, be separated from one another by space or time. They would be in simultaneous existence, occurring in the same instant, but would be separated from each other by the speed differences of their respective quantum steps. This suggests the existence of a fifth dimension in the Universe, beyond the four dimensions of space and time, which could be described as the dimension of speed. Each quantum reality would be separated by this fifth dimension of speed.

The dimension of speed begins at zero and goes up to the critical speed of each quantum reality. However, this zero point should not be confused by the state of non-movement which we experience with matter. This is merely an illusion of rest set up by the vortex.

Each critical speed of movement would represent the demarcation between one quantum step of reality and the next in the dimension of speed. For example, the speed of light would represent the demarcation between the physical and other realities. As such it could be described as the *light barrier*. All speeds are measured from zero. This could be described as the common ground point of all movements. If the Universe consists of a series of quantum realities based upon different critical speeds of movement, then because they all share the same ground point, they would be concentric about this point.

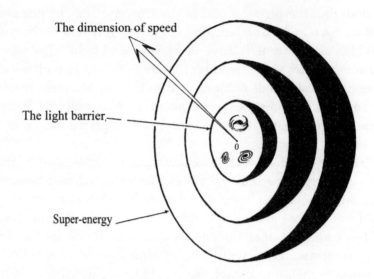

**Fig. 9.2** *The fifth dimension of speed*

Because there is no space-time separation between physical and *super-physical* quantum realities, a field of energy from another quantum reality could coincide with a physical body. Each body in the physical part of the Universe could have, associated with it, a super-energy field from each of the quantum realities in the ascending series. This concept of super-energy fields, associated with the physical body, would correspond to the orgone energy described by Wilhelm Reich, the *morphic fields* of Rupert Sheldrake, the *life-fields* described by Harold Saxton Burr and the *aura* described by healers and psychics.

If the super-energy fields are based on vortex and wave structures, they would have many of the properties of electric and magnetic fields based on vortices and waves of physical energy. From electro-static research it is clear that electric fields are evenly distributed over spheres. However, if there is a spike on the sphere, the charge will accumulate on the spike and a potential difference will occur between the spike and the sphere. Energy, in the form of electricity, flows along the potential gradient. This electro-static principle should also operate in the super-energy fields.

If a super-energy field follows the contours of the physical body, then the electro-static principles would suggest the occurrence of potential gradients between the main body of the field - aligned with the head and torso - and appendages to the field - aligned with the fingers, feet and ears. Super-energy would then be expected to flow along these gradients. In fact, Burr did measure potential gradients between the limbs and the body, and the predicted flow lines of super-energy corresponded closely to acupuncture meridians. The Chinese discovered that there are specific *meridians*, which run from the fingers, feet and ears, to every organ in the body. In *Acupuncture*, tissues in the body are treated by stimulating or sedating the flow of super-energy - described by the Chinese as *Chi* - in these meridians. The insertion of needles, into specific sites (called acupuncture points) on the meridians, represents only one form of acupuncture. In the method, known as *Acupressure*, the flow of Chi is influenced by massaging specific acupressure points on the meridians. Logic would suggest that if the organ-specific meridians terminate on the soles of the feet, then acupressure on the terminal points would effect another form of therapy. Such a therapy exists. It is called *Reflexology*.

In 1986, the British Medical Association published a report on alternative medicine. Whilst they could not deny that alternative therapies were effective, they could not support them because they were considered to be unscientific. The BMA had especial difficulty in accommodating reflexology - they could find no rational basis to that therapy at all. It is clear to me that the fault lies not with alternative medicine or reflexology but with the outmoded scientific paradigm endorsed by the BMA. With the new scientific framework it is easy to accommodate the alternative therapies.

From the standpoint of *the new science of the spirit*, hand healing, faith healing or the 'laying on of hands' can be understood as the direct transfer of super-energy from the field of the healer to the field of the patient. Absent healing is possible because the super-energy fields exist outside of physical space and time and so the physical separation between the healer and the patient has no bearing on the field interactions.

*Homoeopathy* can also be accommodated by the new scientific paradigm. Homoeopathy was founded 180 years ago by a German, Dr Hahnemann, on the principle of 'like cures like'. Hahnemann found that if a substance, that caused a particular set of symptoms, was greatly diluted, the diluted form of the substance would cure the symptoms. For example, arsenic will cause severe stomach pains but Hahnemann found that a dilution of arsenic will cure stomach pain. Hahnemann discovered that the more he diluted his remedies, the more effective they became. However, the secret in his method was a process he called *potentising*. On each dilution he potentised his remedies by percussing them to release and increase the energy associated with them.

I suggest that homoeopathy operates on the principle that 'anti-like cures like'. I believe that the potentising process acts in a similar way to photography. In the potentising, the super-energy field of the substance that causes the symptoms is impressed on the super-energy field of the *substrate*, in which it is diluted. The field pattern of the substance acts as a positive and in the potentising process it creates a super-energy negative. With increased dilution and potentisation, the positive is decreased and the negative increased; the concentration of symptom-causing substance is reduced whilst the quantity of anti-symptom substrate is increased. This is why homoeopathic remedies become more effective as they are diluted and potentised. The important point is that homoeopathic medicines act energetically rather than chemically. Like most other alternative therapies, homoeopathy is concerned with treating the physical body through the life-field.

I believe the key to understanding the alternative therapies and the way that super-energy can be harnessed in our physical world, lies in a *resonance* process which I describe as *super-energy resonance*. This could also be described as an *inter-reality resonance* as it occurs between different levels of quantum reality. For those who describe these levels as 'dimensions', this key interactive process could be called *interdimensional* or *multi-dimensional resonance*.

Resonance is simple to understand. A mechanical system which is free to move, like a taught string, a diving board, a wooden bridge or the air in a pipe, has a natural frequency of vibration which depends upon its characteristic shape or form. When a periodic force of the same frequency is applied to the system it goes into resonance and the amplitude of vibration becomes large. For example, if a diving board is bent and then allowed to vibrate freely, it oscillates at its own natural frequency. As a diver jumps on the board, the board is forced to vibrate at the frequency of the jumps. The amplitude of these forced vibrations is low. However, when the frequency of jumps reaches the natural frequency of the board, resonance occurs. The amplitude of vibration of the board suddenly becomes very large and the diver is propelled into a dive.

Resonance also occurs when a tuning fork is sounded in a room with a piano. The waves of sound from the tuning fork will cause piano strings, tuned to the same note, to vibrate. When the fork vibrates, it sets up waves of sound in the air. These overlap the piano strings and if strings are tuned to match the sound waves in their wave form, an exchange of energy occurs between them. Energy passes down a gradient from the sound waves to the strings and sets them in motion.

Information is transmitted by resonance in radio and television. Radio and television waves are broadcast with a specific frequency. Information is carried on the wave as a distortion or *modulation* of its form. As it overlays an electrical coil and condenser circuit tuned to its frequency, resonance occurs. An electrical vibration is set up within the circuit in sympathy with the modulated wave form. The electrical signal is then amplified and transformed into sound or a visual image which represents the broadcast information.

Resonance could easily occur between super-physical and physical realities because there is no space-time separation between them. All forms of super-energy would, in effect, coincide with every form of physical energy but normally no interaction would occur between them. However, if a form of energy in our world happens to match a form in super-energy, resonance could occur between them. Energy could pass down the activity gradient between matching forms of super-energy and physical energy, to cause the appearance of energy or information in our world, in apparent defiance of the Laws of Thermodynamics. The ascending series of quantum realities would provide the gradient down which energy could pass in the resonance process.

In *The Vortex : Key to Future Science*, I suggested that the life-fields associated with living organisms could interact with cells via a resonance with DNA.

The concept of *DNA resonance* was then used to suggest an underlying mechanism for many of the alternative therapies and to account for intelligent direction of the processes of evolution and differentiation. Assuming intelligence to be a universal phenomenon, through DNA resonance intelligent information could come into the physical from the super-physical worlds, to engineer genetics and bring about the diversity of life on Earth.

In his book, *The Intelligent Universe*, Fred Hoyle argued for intelligence as the driving force behind the process of evolution. He spoke of the gods in Greek mythology as a model for managers of the Universe. In *The Vortex : Key to Future Science*, Peter Hewitt pointed to the symbolism of resonance in the pipes of Pan for the mechanism of DNA resonance, which we believed to be the key to evolution.

The resonance that occurs in a pipe, or between a tuning fork and piano strings, or a diver and a diving board, could be described as wave resonance because it occurs between oscillating systems. Super-energy resonance could occur between oscillating systems, especially through resonant electrical circuits. At certain frequencies of electro-magnetic oscillation, super-energy resonance should occur as a spontaneous phenomenon. This would happen as the circuit tunes into a super-energy wave-form oscillation of a comparable frequency. This type of resonance could provide a theoretical basis for the alternative therapy system known as *Radionics*.

If the vortex is as fundamental a form in nature as the wave, then resonance should also occur between matching vortices as well as matching waves. If this occurs, such a process could be called *vortex resonance*.

There are many different types of vortex in the physical part of the Universe, including the spherical vortex - modelled by a ball of wool - and conical vortex - modelled by the whirlpool. If the symmetry of 'as above, so below' applies and the laws of physics and forms of energy are much the same in the different quantum realities, then vortices should also be prevalent in the realms of super-energy. If this were so then it should be possible to create vortices in our world which match vortices existing beyond the light barrier. With no space-time separation between vortices of physical energy and super-energy, these would coincide and super-energy resonance could then occur between them.

Setting up a vortex for super-energy resonance would be equivalent to tuning a piano string for wave resonance so this could be described as 'tuning the vortex'. A piano string is tuned by varying its physical characteristics such as its length, tension and diameter. A vortex would be tuned by varying its speed and its physical characteristics such as its shape and the properties of the spinning medium.

If a vortex, with optimal physical characteristics, is set in motion and its speed is steadily increased, then at a certain threshold speed inter-reality resonance should begin to occur. Once resonance starts, the energy of the vortex should increase exponentially. The exponential input of energy would occur because one feature of resonance is that there is no limit to the number of individual systems that can be involved in a single resonance process. This is illustrated by radio and television. There is no limit to the number of radio or television sets that can resonate to a single broadcast. With no space-time separation between physical energy and super-energy, a physical vortex could resonate with every single matching super-physical vortex in existence. By doing so, the physical vortex could draw a virtually unlimited amount of energy into our world from the super-physical realms of the Universe. I believe vortex resonance is the operating principle of the super-energy generators.

Vortex resonance is ideal for the production of electrical and mechanical power because it involves rotational motion. It is relatively easy to drive a turbine by vortex resonance and inventors with limited funding and facilities appear to have been able to build operational vortex turbines.

A vortex turbine is constructed to draw a fluid or flux into vortex motion. The turbine is set into motion by a starter-motor using a normal power source. Once spinning, its speed is steadily increased until a threshold speed is achieved. If vortex resonance occurs, then the turbine would begin to accelerate of its own accord - at that point the starter-motor should be allowed to disengage.

Resonant systems need to be *damped* to prevent them going out of control - in wave resonance to prevent the amplitude of vibration becoming infinitely large and in vortex resonance to prevent the speed of vortex motion increasing indefinitely. Vortex resonance could be damped by an arrangement that changes the physical characteristics of the vortex to take it out of tune. By continually tuning and untuning the vortex, the state of resonance could be kept critical to provide an optimal output of energy and keep the process under control. For example, if the vortex resonance were to occur in air, it might be possible to control the system by varying temperature and pressure. In an electric system the electrical or magnetic characteristics of the supporting circuit could be altered. Alternatively a vortex turbine can be damped by setting up an opposing system of resonance. For example, if a magnetic vortex is set up by spinning a magnet, this could be damped by coupling it with a magnetic spinning in the opposite direction.

The predictions of super-energy resonance have led me to a series of speculations about the structure of the Universe. Most of my ideas about the Universe, beyond the speed of light, are impossible to verify experimentally, however, I feel they are a valuable addition to the book because they lead to an understanding of the traditional view of the Universe held by metaphysicians, and mystics, down through the ages. Personally I have great confidence in esoteric knowledge which has been shunned by science and it is a major objective of my work to redefine the wisdom teachings of the ancients in terms of my vortex hypothesis.

Chapter 10

# THE VORTEX
# UNIVERSE

*"The highest wisdom has but one science, the science of the whole, the science explaining the whole of creation and man's place in it."*

Leo Tolstoy

The Universe can be represented by a conical vortex in which each turn of the spiral represents a plane or level of reality. The base of the cone would represent physical reality and the other turns of the spiral would delineate the ascending series of quantum realities - which I believe to be a *Fibonacci series*.

In a conical vortex, acceleration occurs from the base to the apex. The picture of the Universe as a conical vortex illustrates the acceleration of energy from the lower to the higher levels of reality with each complete turn of the spiral denoting a new, critical speed of activity, giving rise to a distinct world of energy. If the physical is the first quantum level in the Universe, then the second quantum level would correspond to the life-field or morphic field. I believe that the third and fourth quantum levels correspond to what we perceive as emotional and mental realities. (Occultists generally refer to these, respectively, as the *astral* and *psychic* levels of reality.) The life-field, mental and emotional realities are part of our common experience in the physical Universe so I describe the second, third and fourth levels of the

Universe as the *hyper-physical* quantum realities. These correspond to the astral realms of the Universe, as described in the occult sciences. Most psychic phenomena are caused by hyper-physical energies. For example, I would describe a ghost as a hyper-physical body which has survived the death of the physical body.

I treat the Universe as a system of thirteen quantum realities. Beyond the physical there are the three hyper-physical realms of energy. Beyond these there are nine more quantum realities, that I describe as super-physical quantum realities. These correspond to the 'spiritual realms' of the Universe, as described in the occult sciences. The physical is divided from the hyper-physical by the light barrier and the hyper-physical is separated from the super-physical by what I describe as the *psychic barrier*. I believe that most occult and spiritualist phenomena are hyper-physical rather than super-physical, psychic rather than truly spiritual.

The mind is not entirely hyper-physical, rather, the psychic

*Fig. 10.1 The Vortex Universe*

mind is a lower manifestation of universal mind. However, higher levels of mind have to pass through the hyper-physical before they reach the physical and so are subject to distortion by the psychic mind. The psychic or hyper-physical mind - originating in the fourth level of quantum reality - is what we experience as the ego-self. I believe that the emotions are a denser or lower level of psychic phenomena corresponding to slower energies than our normal thoughts. What we perceive as emotions are wave and vortex forms in a super-energy field belonging to the third level of quantum reality. (The psychic barrier exists as a quarantine for the ego-self.)

In the same way that wave energy transmits information in our world so our thoughts and emotions would correspond to radiant energy, and vibrations in the super-energy fields of the hyper-physical levels of reality. Then in the same way that vortex structures store information in our world so our memories would correspond to electro-magnetic fields and structures akin to atomic matter, in those same realms of reality. The combination of waves and vortices in these realities could create worlds as real as the world of matter and light in which we live. The world of the emotions, which we experience as feelings, and the world of the mind, which we perceive as dreams, fantasies and abstractions, would be no less real than the solid structures that surround us. If this is true then mental constructs could be made to appear in our world as real, solid objects. By the power of pure visualisation, bodies could be created and projected anywhere in the Universe.

Contrary to popular scientific belief, I do not hold that the mind and emotions are mere by-products of neurophysiology. I believe that they are universal forms of energy which express themselves through the nervous systems of living organisms. Nor do I perceive *Life* as a by-product of cellular biochemistry. I contend that Life is the primary reality in the Universe and the source of energy at every level within it.

If the Universe exists as a dream, I see Life as the dreamer. If the Universe is the creation then, in my book, Life is the creator. I am the creation of Life. Any other statement is, to my way of thinking, a creation myth. Others can argue over the existence of God, but to me, the existence of Life is undeniable. Life is my God, and the idea that Life is the consequence, rather than the cause of biology, is a popular scientific speculation to which I do not subscribe. My speculation is that Life is the prime reality which expresses itself through the myriad particles of activity that make up the Universe. It brings these into existence as an infinite number of conscious acts of will. These countless acts of abstraction are what we call particles of energy, but Life is not energy, in my book, Life is the source of energy.

Energy is particulate but Life is one. This to me is obvious because each type of energy-particle is uniform. For example, all protons throughout the Universe are identical in their physical characteristics. They all have the same value of mass, spin, charge etc. If protons exist as products of Life then their precise uniformity suggests that there is but one universal Life underlying them all. Each proton and electron, photon and neutron exists as an act of the one, indivisible Life. It is the one, indivisible Life that is conscious in every particle of energy, every rock and stone, every plant and animal, every man, woman and child and every planet, star and galaxy in the Universe. We are all the one Life, living a multitude of experiences in billions of different bodies. This is to me the brother- and sisterhood of man. If you call the creator God then, in your Life, you are God, hidden behind the mask of your ego identity, acting out the drama of your individual existence.

I believe the Universe is a mind and all particles within it are thought forms. The form of a thought is a consequence of intelligence, so I see Life, the originator of thought, as the source of universal intelligence. I do not subscribe to the anthropocentric notion that intelligence is a mere consequence of neurophysiology which reaches its zenith in the human brain. I consider intelligence to be fundamental to all reality. In my philosophy, the forms of wave and vortex are products of the intelligence of Life. They are the basic modules of energy through which Life expresses itself, on which it builds and by means of which it operates. Wave forms of energy can be modulated to transmit information and vortex forms can be organised into fields and structures - such as atoms and molecules. The random interactions of these basic modules, or particles of energy, then establish the freedom in the Universe through which Life can experiment and evolve.

Whilst sub-atomic interactions may appear to be haphazard and random, I believe they are subject to the subtle influences of the hyper-physical, morphic fields. Underlying all physical forms, these fields could allow the conscious direction and experience of Life, at every level of physical formation. They could account for the way that atomic structures are arranged into complex molecules, such as DNA, RNA and proteins - the fabric of living cells in the plant and animal kingdoms. The differentiation of multicellular organisms could also be explained from the invisible influence of hyper-physical fields, through which Life would appear to express itself in the physical realm of the Universe. Through ever more highly organised structures, increasingly complex information can be stored, expressed and assimilated. This is what evolution is all about, but underlying it all is the conscious and intelligent activity of Life, always learning, developing and integrating experiences in its universal playground.

If we look at patterns in the physical part of the Universe, we see that energy is not uniformly distributed. It is concentrated in galaxies, stars and planets. The concentration of particles of energy is associated with a concomitant concentration of particles of hyper-physical super-energy. This is effectively a concentration of modules of the life-field or morphic energy, emotion and psychic mind which allows for a more powerful expression of intelligence in the Universe.

The Universe is a workshop in which, in their random

interactions, particles of energy can bring together modules of hyper-physical energy, in unique and highly experimental formations. Through these novel super-energy formations, new situations can be exploited by intelligence and experienced through feeling and conscious awareness. I am certain that even stones have a level of sensitivity and awareness, through super-energy fields. In the universal workshop, Life is exploiting and learning from every situation that arises through the freedom that randomness allows. We see this principle operating in the evolutionary cycle on Earth, but I do not believe that Life and evolution are confined to organic structures or to the Earth. To me, Life is a universal phenomenon that is present at every level of existence.

The presence of Life throughout the Universe can be understood from the quantum and *fractal* principles. The quantum principle, that *the whole is a collective of parts*, operates throughout the Universe. For example, the Universe exists as a collective of parts. It is a body of galaxies which are, in turn, spiral congregations of stars and planets. On a planet, such as the Earth, a bio-sphere occurs as a collective of unnumerable populations of living organisms, most of which are multitudes of living cells. The planet is itself a collective of molecules and atoms which are, in turn, systems of sub-atomic particles.

The fractal or *hologram* principle, that *the whole is represented in the parts*, is also fundamental to the structure of the Universe. It is represented in the symmetry of 'as above, so below' and 'as below, so above'. The fractal principle, which is central to chaos theory, is illustrated by the *Mandelbrot set*. In 1979, Benoit Mandelbrot discovered a method of feeding the answer to an equation back into the equation to produce, on a computer, an endlessly repeating pattern. Appearing as an intricate order of discs surrounded by 'galactic' swirls and spirals this, now famous pattern, was named after him. The central discs of the Mandelbrot set are edged with minute projections, each of which can be expanded into a repeat of the original pattern. This fractal then repeats itself endlessly.

Applied to the model of the Vortex Universe, the fractal or hologram principle could be used to explain, not only how Life is expressed in every part of the Universe, but how it is collectively conscious of everything. In the model of the Vortex Universe, Life is depicted at the apex of a conical vortex. From that position it expresses itself through an ever increasing number of parts, as the spiral expands out from the point to the base of the cone. At the apex of the cone, Life is portrayed as *One-self* - One fully self-conscious, intelligent reality - existing as the source of an infinite number of selves, fanning out in a network below it. The pyramid is another model for this principle. The model of a pyramid or cone shows how a small number of expressions of Life, in the higher realities of the Universe, can occur as collectives of ever more numerous expressions of Life, lower down in the Universe. The terms *'higher'* and *'lower'*, applied to selves, would denote

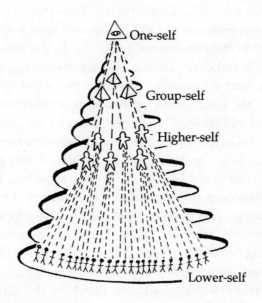

*Fig. 10.2 The Universal fractal*

positions in the pyramid rather than superiority or inferiority. Each self-conscious expression of life would have the same potential, regardless of its position in the Universe. These concepts can be illustrated by the analogy of a pyramid network of octopuses.

Imagine an octopus floating on the surface of the ocean, with its tentacles outstretched below. At the end of each tentacle is another octopus with tentacles spreading out and connecting to yet more octopuses below it. This pattern then repeats itself until billions of octopuses are connected, in the pyramid network, to the original octopus at the surface. Some octopuses may be higher in the pyramid than others but because every octopus is the same as every other octopus, they would not be lesser or greater than those above or below them. The Mandelbrot set also illustrates this point. Each element of the fractal is as fabulous and intricate as the original pattern and each element is essential to the overall pattern. With the loss of a single, minute element, the fractal would be incomplete. This shows that each self-conscious expression of Life, in the universal fractal, is equally important to the Universe as a whole. In the universal order of things, each and every atom is as as significant as a galaxy.

In the Vortex Universe, I describe the uppermost expressions of Life as the *Group-selves*, representing a collective of the larger number of middle level, *Higher-self* beings who represent, in their turn, the collective consciousness of more numerous *Lower-self* beings, existing in the lower realities. Through the fractal principle, Life could be simultaneously conscious through every being in existence and experience the sum total of everything that is happening. This point is illustrated by the octopus analogy. A signal from any octopus in the pyramid could be fed back, via the connecting tentacles, to the primary octopus. That particular cephalopod would thus act as the collector of information from the entire network. I like to think of the Universe as an *interdimensional fractal* which is open and endlessly growing, and evolving from the experiences of each and every component part.

As well as the vortex I also work with the model of the Universe as a system of concentric spheres, which could be imagined as nesting inside each other like Russian dolls. In this model, each quantum reality is represented by one of the spheres. The common centre of the series of spheres represents zero motion. The radius of each sphere represents the speed value of the energy that forms it and the surface of each sphere represents the four dimensions of space and time belonging to that level of reality. The fifth dimension of speed is represented by the radial separation between each successive, concentric sphere. This model - which shows the physical part of the Universe as the smallest, innermost sphere - illustrates the greater quantum realities containing all the lesser realities in the series.

The concentric sphere model is based on the simple principle that greater speeds contain all lesser speeds. It shows the higher quantum realities, based upon faster speeds, as greater spheres. These contain the lower realities in the series, based upon slower speeds, which are shown as the lesser concentric spheres. In the movement Universe, quantum realities are created out of successively higher speeds of energy, so this principle is of vital importance. Because the speed of light is a *sub-set* of the higher multiples of the speed of light, everything relative to the speed of light would be a sub-set or a part of the higher quantum realities. For example, physical space and time would be a sub-set or part of hyper-physical space and time. Then, of course, these hyper-physical realities would, in their turn, be part of the super-physical realities beyond them. I perceive our world as being but a small part of the unseen worlds of super-energy, existing beyond the speed of light.

The first and innermost sphere represents the physical plane of reality. The second sphere would be the *morphic plane* of reality, the third sphere the *astral plane* and the fourth sphere, the *psychic plane* of reality. The four innermost spheres represent the physical and the hyper-physical realities. There would then be nine concentric spheres extending beyond them, representing the nine

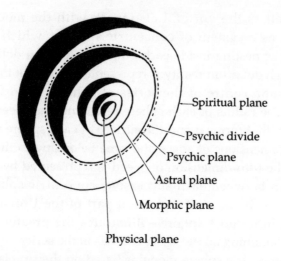

*Spiritual plane*
*Psychic divide*
*Psychic plane*
*Astral plane*
*Morphic plane*

Physical plane

**Fig. 10.3** *The concentric sphere model for the Universe*

planes of super-physical quantum reality.

With no space-time separation between the different realities in the Universe, they would all be totally coincident. Therefore, as I have already explained, every particle and atom, molecule and cell, body, planet, star and galaxy could be overlaid or overshadowed by hyper-physical and super-physical fields or bodies - which, for simplicity, I call the super-energy fields or bodies.

The view that a physical body contains a super-energy field, or a super-energy body, is incorrect because the sub-set principle shows that it is the super-energy realities which contain the physical reality as a lesser part. We should therefore see ourselves as super-energy beings possessing physical bodies, rather than physical beings possessing super-energy bodies.

Sub-atomic particles are arranged into atoms, which are, in turn, arranged into molecules, cells and multicellular bodies. I believe this organisation occurs through the morphic fields acting as a field matrix responsible for the forms in our world - each morphic *field matrix* acting as a template or blueprint for the structures in our world from atoms to galaxies and viruses to multi-cellular organisms.

Each higher reality could be acting as a blueprint or field matrix for the forms and structures in lower realities below them to produce the effect of *layered field matrices*. Thus, for example, a psychic field could act as a blueprint for the emotional body which could, in its turn, influence the form of the morphic field. The effect of layered field matrices on the forms and structures of the Universe can be understood through analogy with holograms. If Life is portrayed as 'the light of consciousness' one could imagine it illuminating the super-energy blueprints, like a laser light shining through holographic films. Just as the laser light produces a three -dimensional image or hologram from the holographic film, so each super-energy field or body would exist as the equivalent of a hologram, produced by the light of consciousness shining through the field matrix above it. At the same time it could act as the holographic film or field matrix for the hologram projections in the reality below it.

To my mind, each electron and proton, photon and enetron, in the physical realm, exists as a holographic insert. Each is an abstract image inserted in our world by the laser light of Life shining through its holographic blueprint in the morphic realm of the Universe. This explains how Life creates the world of physical energy as an illusion. I perceive the physical world as a *quantum hologram*, projected from the hyper-physical realms.

The fundamental error in the atomic hypothesis and the materialism that stems from it, is the false doctrine that the physical realm of matter and light, space and time is an independent reality which exists of itself and nothing else. The new quantum hypothesis suggests that the Universe is a *virtual reality* which is dependant upon consciousness. I believe that as self-conscious beings we are in danger of becoming trapped in the virtual reality by believing it to be objectively real. I contend that through attachment to the material hypothesis and denial of unseen realities, science is acting in ignorance and supporting a trap of illusion.

I like to imagine the Earth as a *flight simulator,* designed to train pilots of consciousness to fly in the physical realm of light and matter. The problem for us, as the pilots, is the simulator is so effective at appearing to be real that on entering it, we are liable to forget it is only a simulator. Believing the simulator to be the sole reality we are frightened to leave it. Through fear and ignorance we become trapped in the simulator and forego the freedom to enter and leave it at will.

Unseen worlds of super-energy could provide an account for the spiritual realities, purported to exist as parallel worlds to our own. Devas, gods and angels, which have been dismissed as superstitious nonsense by materialistic science, could correspond to a primitive description of conscious and intelligent, super-physical entities.

Elementals and nature spirits would correspond to the hyper-physical levels of field matrix organisation in our world. Animated by the laser light of Life, projected from the higher levels of super-energy in the universal fractal - known as devas, gods or angels - they would be responsible for order in the plant and animal kingdoms. These in their turn would correspond to the super-physical field matrices animated by the laser light of consciousness projected by the greater gods or archangels in the quantum realities above them. The spiritual hierarchies would thus represent the layered field matrices of the universal fractal through which Life consciousness projects order from the highest into the lowest levels of the Universe.

The idea of gods and nature spirits is common to the belief systems of all indigenous people throughout the world. The contempt for ancient wisdom teachings and traditional folklore, so prevalent in our materialistic age, is a symptom of ignorance rather than advance in knowledge. In fact, there is much in common between modern and traditional modes of belief. Unseen spirits have their parallel in the virtual particles of quantum mechanics and the quarks which have never been seen. The forms may have changed as science has come to replace religion but man's belief in unseen realities is as strong as ever.

It is part of all pre-scientific, religious and native traditions that we share the Earth with invisible beings in unseen worlds and it is interesting to note that in these traditions, speed was taken to be the factor separating the physical from the spiritual beings. In common folklore, humans were considered to be separated from spiritual entities by speed of movement. For example, it was said that we don't see the fairies because we are too slow and clumsy and the angels are all around us but we don't see them because they are moving too fast.

Whilst I appreciate the scientific community may be reluctant to entertain the idea of angels and fairies as a scientific reality and may not be predisposed to rewrite their textbooks around fairies instead of quarks, these spiritual traditions of humanity are persistent. Persistent ideas are not affected by the fickle tides of fashions in thought. Like rocks, they stand the test of time - though for periods they may be submerged and lost from view. Myths appear like castles of sand which last until the tide of thinking changes and then they are swept away. Just because spiritual ideas are out of fashion in our modern scientific age does not mean they are false. On the contrary, I believe that the spiritual has been submerged by the material in order to test its worth. Whatever spirituality survives the onslaught of materialistic science will have proved true. Science could be thought of as a fire which engulfs all systems of knowledge. In the process, dross is consumed but gold remains unchanged. In *the new science of the spirit*, the fairy lore of humanity appears unscathed. All that has changed is language. In place of words like spirit or etheric I use words like super-energy or hyper-physical reality. Instead of elemental, I speak of hyper-physical hologram. Thus I endeavour to make these ancient ideas slightly more palatable to people of scientific bent. For those who complain they have never seen a fairy - after all, seeing is believing - my reply is that we are living on one! The watery planet Earth is the present embodiment of an ondine or water sprite we have come to call Gaia. In our watery bodies we are her children and in our science we have been more preoccupied with the study of this fairy being, and her offspring, than anything else in the Universe!

If the hologram principle - that the whole is represented in every part - is applied to the Universe then energy patterns that apply to the Universe as a whole will apply to galaxies and stars, planets and people and vice versa. The pattern of a series of super-energy states coinciding with the physical would be the same with us as it is with the Universe and also with the planet. The planet would have hyper-physical energy fields associated with it which could be described as its morphic, astral and psychic bodies. It would also have super-energy fields associated with it which could be described as its spirit. Therefore, to talk of the planet as a living embodiment of spirit is no different to talking of a person in that same way and it is worth noting that most native and shamanistic traditions treat the Earth with respect, because they consider her to be a living being. Only men and women in the materialistic age treat the Earth as a non-living body of matter, to be exploited and plundered, and it is this so-called 'scientific attitude' which is leading to her destruction.

The hologram principle also leads to another fascinating idea. I have already established that hyper-physical and super-physical realities can coincide with the physical - being separated from it only by the intrinsic speed of their energy. Existing in their own space and time, the extension of bodies in these realities need have no bearing on the extension of a physical body, or vice versa. Therefore, we could experience a super-energy body as a point, whilst in its own reality it could be as big as a planet, so a super-energy body could be experienced, simultaneously, as contracting into a point and extending out as a field. I have described the Universe in terms of a conical vortex contracting inwards and a system of concentric spheres extending outward. The hologram principle would suggest that these two models should apply to the way we perceive our own super-energy

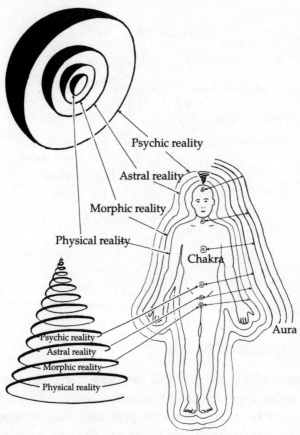

Psychic reality

Astral reality

Morphic reality

Physical reality

Chakra

Psychic reality
Astral reality
Morphic reality
Physical reality

Aura

***Fig. 10.4*** *Man and the Universe*

bodies. If I am correct in my models for the Universe, we should experience each super-energy body as a field extending outward and a vortex contracting inwards. In fact this is precisely the way that our super-energy bodies have been perceived in the healing and natural medicine traditions. Sometimes they are experienced as a field of subtle energy extending outward from the body - described as the aura. Sometimes they are perceived as a vortex of subtle energy contracting into the body - described as a *chakra*.

For each hyper-physical and super-physical energy body, associated with the physical, there is an energy vortex and an

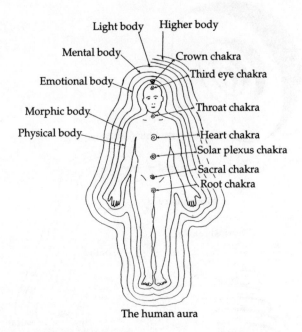

The human aura

*Fig. 10.5* Chakras and the aura

energy field, which are one and the same thing. If, beyond the physical realm, there are twelve quantum realities associated with the Universe, then the hologram principle would suggest that there are twelve super-energy fields and chakras associated with a human body.

If we consider the hyper-physical bodies as super-energy vortices or chakras then the body of morphic energy would correspond to the base chakra. The base chakra is associated with sexuality, and therefore, morphic energy is experienced in the orgasm. This would explain why Wilhelm Reich described it as orgone energy. The second chakra, in the sacral position, would correspond to the emotional or astral body. The third chakra, in the solar plexus position, would correspond to the mental or psychic body and the fourth chakra, in the heart position, would correspond to the lightbody. The next three chakras in the throat, forehead and crown positions, correspond to the three, higher bodies of super-physical energy which are intended to be integrated with the physical body. The five remaining chakras, above the crown, are not normally integrated with the physical body.

The law that lesser speeds of motion are an integral part of the greater speeds has an important bearing on the super-energy fields and chakras. It would seem obvious, from this law, that being part of the greater, a lesser level of energy would be governed by the greater levels. The operation of this principle is clear from the relationship between the physical body and the morphic field. The morphic field governs the physical body, being responsible for its morphogenesis and differentiation, health and integrity. It would follow that the emotional or astral body governs the morphic field. This would explain why the emotions have such an impact on health and why emotional stress is a major factor in disease. The mental body should govern the emotional body, thus the emotions should surrender to reason and the power of the will. However, the mental body should, in its turn, be governed by the super-physical, *spirit body*. When humans deny the spirit, the mind and emotions run amok and this weakens the morphic body and the impact of this, on the control of differentiation, is clearly seen in the increase in degenerative diseases - such as cancer - in our materialistic day and age. Materialism is destroying us physically and spiritually, as it is destroying the Earth.

The laws of motion also predicts that  physical energy cannot interact with the super-energy because the super-energy exists outside of physical space-time - whereas super-energy could interact with physical forms because the physical realm is a part of super-energy space and time. It follows that waves of physical energy would not reflect off super-energy objects so these objects could not be seen in our world. However, waves of super-energy could reflect off physical objects and so the physical world would be visible from the realms of super-energy. (The coincidence of hyper-physical and super-physical realities with the physical allows for the existence of civilisations on planets that appear to us to be devoid of life and in stars which would disrupt physical life. For these super-energy civilisations, the planet or star would be an integral part of their environment even though, for we observers in the physical, the super-energy civilisation would be invisible.)

These ideas are supported by reports of near-death experiences. The reports of near-death experiences are generally dismissed or explained away by establishment scientists as hallucinations, caused by oxygen starvation to the brain. Nonetheless, people have returned from the brink of death, in an operation or an accident, thanks to modern methods of resuscitation. During the experience they claim to have looked down on their bodies and whilst they could see people in the physical world, these people were unaware of them. This circumstantial evidence supports the idea that super-energy can interact with physical objects, whereas physical energy does not interact with bodies of super-energy.

Near-death experiences, which are now very common, can be accommodated in a reasonable framework of understanding and treated as empirical observations to support the *new science of the spirit*. The near-death reports also support the idea that emotional and mental faculties survive death, as embodiments of conscious Life, and that by means of these faculties the physical world can be perceived from an after-death state of existence.

# Chapter 11

# ASCENSION

*"All life is one and all its manifestations with which we have contact are climbing the ladder of evolution."*

Lord Dowding

I have my own views on the issues of physical life and death. I believe that, in the formation of the Universe, conscious Life went through a process which could be described as *branching*. Branching is another way of conceptualising the one Life, as the figurative laser light of consciousness, shining through an ever increasing number of energy holograms further out from its source. This branching enabled an ever increasing number of energetic entities to come into existence, in the expansion of the fractal Universe from the super-physical to the hyper-physical and from the hyper-physical out into the physical. I like to depict this in the conceptual model of *Life-strands*.

As the Life-strands reach out into the Universe, branching again and again, they would animate the energetic forms and retrieve conscious experience through them. Through the many forms of energy it is always the one Life expressing itself. Life-strands from the one-self establish a number of group-selves which then branch into a multitude of higher-selves. Life-strands from these then animate the hosts of lower-selves, evident in physical populations.

As a Life-strand descends from a higher-self into the hyper-physical realms, you could picture this aspect of universal consciousness dressing itself, first in psychic energy, then emotional, then morphic energy and finally, adorning itself in physical matter, to become an embryo in the mother's womb. I like the image of the body and its ego personality as a space suit that the Life-strand of consciousness has donned, to enable it to survive and function on the surface of a planet. The super-energy aspects of the space suit provide feeling and cognitive abilities and the physical body provides a unique genetic inheritance. This, with the circumstances in which the new individual finds itself after birth, offers Life a unique opportunity to gain experience of the plane of physical reality.

On death, the physical body decays, leaving the morphic, emotional and psychic bodies to revert to the hyper-physical realms of the Universe. In my view these constitute the *soul*. This super-energy counterpart to the physical body, lingering near the Earth after physical death, corresponds to the *ghost*. During life on earth, the psychic and emotional energies would be moulded into bodies that are as real as the physical. Memories are vortex structures in hyper-physical energy, the equivalent of matter. Thoughts and feelings are vibrations in emotional and psychic energy, the equivalent of heat, light and sound.

Following the principle of branching, a Life-strand from a higher-self - which in my paradigm constitutes the spirit - could establish a number of lower-selves to set up a series of unique incarnations. If these were strung out through successive generations, the higher-self would benefit from the experience of different cultures in the evolution of human society. I call these *consecutive incarnations*. However, if it serves the higher-self to have a number of different experiences in the same generation, then there is no reason why it should not have *simultaneous incarnations*. This means that the same Life-strand would be animating several different bodies and souls, at the same time. From the perspective of the higher-self, existing outside of physical space and time, all incarnations are in simultaneous existence. It is only we who differentiate physical time into the

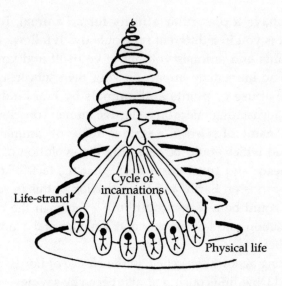

**Fig. 11.1** *The incarnating Life-strand*

past, present and future. So for the higher-self, apart from cultural experience, there would be no difference between simultaneous or consecutive incarnations.

Life-strands from the same higher-self in the super-physical realms of the Universe, could animate a number of different types of body at the same time to serve its different experiential requirements - much as we don different types of clothing for different purposes. You, as a spirit-self, could be existing in plant and animal bodies as well as human bodies to gain the maximum spectrum of experience - in the same or in different times. It is absurd to rank beings according to their outfits. For example, our ranking the cat body as superior to the human body, for the incarnation of spirit, is as shallow as ranking a man in a city-suit superior to a man in a boiler suit. An alien, looking objectively at life on Earth, might consider cats superior to humans and perceive us as a species domesticated by cats rather than vice versa. Cats, after all, have we humans trained to provide for all their needs whilst retaining a lofty independence of us. If you find you have a particular affinity for an animal, it could be because it is you in a different type of body. It follows that if you abuse plants and animals you abuse yourself and your actions will have an immediate impact on your own subconscious. The collective abuse of plants and animals by mankind could be having a devastating effect on collective human consciousness.

In the name of science, a serious abuse of animals is being perpetrated which could be retarding the evolution of humanity toward peace and freedom. I think that the lack of respect for other life-forms on Earth, and the reflection of this in science and industry, could be a major contributing factor in the collapse of our civilisation into lawlessness and violence and I am not alone in this belief.

Speaking against *vivisection*, in the House of Lords, on July 18, 1957, Lord Dowding concluded his speech by saying:

"All life is one and all its manifestations with which we have contact are climbing the ladder of evolution...It is an important part of our responsibilities to help them in their ascent, and not to retard their development by cruel exploitation of their helplessness.

"What I am now saying, if people would realise it, is of great practical importance, because failure to recognise our responsibilities towards the animal kingdom is the cause of many of the calamities which beset the nations of the world. Nearly all of us have a deep-rooted wish for peace - peace on Earth; but we shall never attain to true peace - the peace of love, and not the uneasy equilibrium of fear - until we recognise the place of animals in the scheme of things and treat them accordingly."

As the Life-strand in each individual being originates from the same one-self - the same consciousness is incarnate in every life-form - we all belong to the same group subconscious. We cannot harm another living organism without harming ourselves, therefore it is obvious that we will never experience peace and happiness unless we learn to respect every creature as being another aspect of ourselves.

The one Life reincarnates again and again, in every living form throughout the Universe. Only the ego-self lives in the illusion of separation and perceives other beings as existing apart from itself. Everything in existence is a manifestation of the same Life with the same underlying potential for consciousness, intelligence and love. The illusion of separation from the one Life, the source of all, is the primordial lie at the root of all suffering.

This lie is exacerbated by our experience of time as a separation into past, present and future. All your other lives are programmes of experience and knowledge, which are as real for you as your current lifetime. If, in *regression*, your consciousness is connected into a past-life, it would be alive for you and enable you to live the experience of that lifetime as if it were happening for you now. You would become the person in your past, with all their feelings and experiences. None of the lives in a chain of incarnations are truly separate. As part of a whole, they all influence each other. Even if you are not conscious of these other lives they are still a part of you. They constitute your personal subconscious and the other lives on your Life-strand have a hidden influence on our attitudes, inclinations and pattern of behaviour in this lifetime.

I appreciate that many people believe in life-after-death but not in *reincarnation*. For example, Christians believe that for each incarnation a completely fresh soul is created. For the most part this teaching could be correct. I believe that souls only reincarnate on rare occasions - usually after a premature and often violent death. Cases to support this are cited in *The Vortex : Key to Future Science*. I am of the opinion that generally, after death, the Life-strand breaks away from the soul, shedding first the morphic body then the emotional and psychic bodies, leaving them as an empty shell or psychic hologram. In shedding these it breaks away from attachment to its last incarnation. If it is unable to detach itself, it may linger as a ghost, or if it is fortunate it may reincarnate again. If the Life-strand is unable to release itself from the mental and emotional body it is liable to become trapped in the astral and psychic realms. This would correspond to the concept of souls lost in hell. Within the mind and emotions, each person creates their own heaven or hell whilst on Earth, and it is into that reality of their own creation that they go on death.

If the Life-strand can break free from the discarnate soul then it can take up another incarnation in a fresh soul and a new body. This is reincarnation of the spirit, not the soul. The idea of a new soul as well as a new body, coming into being with each incarnation, was taught by Rudolf Steiner. In his writing he suggested that: "The human spirit is its own species and that just as the life-body reproduces the form from species to species so does the Life-spirit reproduce the soul from personal existence to personal existence."

I see each life on Earth as an opportunity to experiment, change and grow in patterns of thinking and behaviour. This is the way of science, not religion. Religions resist experiment and change in patterns of thinking and behaviour. This is why I believe that it will be through science rather than religion that mankind will find spiritual freedom. Ultimately, each life represents an opportunity to ascend beyond the traps of mind and emotions, into the freedom of the higher levels of super-energy, the super-physical or *spiritual realms* of the Universe.

Each physical life is like a battery that eventually runs out. Each of us battles against time, confronting the challenges of our circumstances, both environmental and genetic. In the end it is what we do with ourselves, in our brief spell on Earth that decides our destiny. The greatest mistake we make is to treat life on Earth as an end in itself; that is the grave error in materialistic science. It takes wisdom to appreciate the Earth is a school we visit, to learn lessons, face challenges and pass tests.

I am certain that the curriculum of the terrestrial school is Love. Not the emotional love we experience in relationships but the care we have for each other when we appreciate we are all the same essential Being dressed in a multitude of different bodies.

Caring for each other and serving the whole follows from this realisation. There is a purpose for human life on Earth. It cannot be the pursuit of knowledge because knowledge is far more easily gained from the higher perspective of the worlds of super-energy which we left in order to come into physical incarnation. It cannot be the pursuit of things because nothing lasts and we can't take anything with us when we go. It cannot be the pursuit of power because this is a situation in the Universe where individual power is most restricted. The major lesson for us here would seem to be to learn how to Love.

Looking at human behaviour today and throughout history shows that the greatest challenge for each individual has been to show unconditional Love. In a situation where we appear to be disconnected from Love, the challenge is to manifest Love for ourselves and others. Relationships are the major battleground - be they between people or nations - and the only solution is and always has been Love.

The illusion of separation that occurs in this world does provide a learning ground for unconditional Love and what we perceive to be evil and destructive could be simply hurdles that we have to overcome. When we have proved our ability to Love, in this difficult test, we can we ascend out of the hyper-physical and into the super-physical realms of the Universe. Look at what we are doing to this planet, without Love, and you will understand why we have to learn to Love and care before we are given greater freedom, power and dominion in the Universe.

As with all schools, when term comes to an end, the pupils have to return home with whatever lessons they have learnt. The way that each has performed determines their career prospects. Some fail and have to repeat the lessons. Others pass and can start at university or perhaps take up a responsible job. The rounds of reincarnation are represented by the days at school. Each reincarnation cycle reaches a time of completion which is represented by the end of term. Just as the term ends with an examination so I believe that the 20th century is the century of examination for the present cycle of human incarnations - and the present world population ensures that all the students can be present for the final test. According Josè Argüelles, the calendar of the ancient Mayan civilisation indicates that our term ends in the year 2012.

Those that have not learnt to Love could join another cycle of incarnations and begin a new term at school. Those who have learnt their lessons of Love will ascend to complete the larger cycle - a cycle that all will eventually complete - though it may take many cycles of incarnation to do so. The completion of the great cycle is the return of the Life-strand back to its true home or *Source.*

As Life-strands extend outward, in the vortex Universe, through the descending levels of self, so eventually they must return through the ascending levels of self, back to the Source again. Without the return or ascent to Source, after a phase of outgoing or descent from the source, Life would be caught in an unending expansion. In nature, Life systems flow in cycles of expansion and contraction which maintain the circles of infinity. The idea of Life-strands returning to Source is as obvious as breathing. Just as the breath has to expire after an inspiration, so Life must eventually return from whence it came to complete a cycle.

Physical reality would seem to be the slowest realm of energy in the Universe. If there were lower realities based on energies less than the speed of light, we would be aware of them because they would constitute a lesser part of physical reality. As it is clear in physics and astronomy that everything in the observable Universe is relative to the speed of light, we can conclude that the physical world is the base of the Vortex Universe. If the physical realm is the furthest outreach of energy in the Universe, it follows that the physical incarnation must represent the extremity of the descent of self-conscious Life into the Universe. Just as the breath changes its stroke when it reaches the extremity of inspiration or expiration, so the return of Life to Source must begin from the physical level of reality; and it begins with the breath.

To ascend it is necessary to direct the Life-strand from the physical and hyper-physical realities into the super-physical realms of the Universe. Each person has the will-power to direct the Life-strand through conscious attention. This can be done through the chakras. Just as the three lower chakras are centres of hyper-physical energies so the fourth or heart chakra is the first centre of super-physical energy. This is the super-energy of the lightbody in the fifth level of quantum reality. As a super-energy field the lightbody has been perceived as a halo - hence its name - and, according to James Hurtak and Jewish mystical traditions, it is described as the *Merkabah*.

In order to ascend it is necessary to establish a firm connection with the Merkabah through the heart chakra. This is achieved by allowing the attention to follow the breath. Within the breath it is possible to feel the super-energy of the heart chakra; the light of the Merkabah. This is generally perceived as a sense of expansiveness, contentment, well-being or peace. On relaxation the breath will go deep and slow of its own accord. To maintain the centre of attention in the breath, rather than in the thoughts and emotions, takes practice. To relax and let go of concerns and preoccupations in order to surrender to the simplicity and tranquillity of the breath requires faith. This is not the religious faith of belief in a doctrine but a trust that there is nothing really to worry about. This comes with the understanding that on Earth, people are being trained, tried and tested in the equivalent of a flight simulator. Difficulties are intended to make, not break, the spirit. All needs will be met and everything is happening for a purpose.

The heart chakra is also important in the demonstration of ability to Love in care and service to others and the whole. In mystical traditions the heart chakra is the centre of Love in each human being. When an individual is centred in the breath, Love for Life, the self and others will well up spontaneously through the heart chakra and break as a fountain of compassion for the benefit of all.  Staying centred in the breath is the greatest service a person  can perform for the benefit of humanity.  Conscious breathing keeps the door to the Spirit open in the human heart. Pouring through this portal, the super-physical energy of the higher self can fill the aura with Love and set the auras of others into empathetic resonance.

The use of conscious breathing to bring about the ascension of consciousness is common to many mystic traditions.  In India it is treated as the supreme yoga, which brings about union with the spirit.  The practice is simple but not easy because of the habit most people have of allowing their attention to follow the hyper-physical patterns, the vibrations in the psychic and emotional bodies.  These thoughts and emotions are constant distractions which act to trap conscious Life in the psychic and astral realms. Depending upon consciousness for Life, thoughts and emotions are like *parasites which* prey on conscious attention.  Individuals identify with them but they are not the individual.  When a person goes beyond thought and emotion they discover who they really are and therein lies their freedom.

In addition to the breath, many mystical traditions - including the yogic way of India and martial arts of China and Japan - recommend that the tongue be kept curled up in the mouth.  This practice brings the conscious attention into the throat chakra.  A sweet taste or tingling around the edge of the tongue, as it is curled back, maintains awareness of this chakra.  The physical process of curling the tongue also serves as a reminder to breathe consciously.

As well as centring in the heart and throat, many mystical traditions speak of the inner light.  Whilst centred on the breath, the individual can close the eyes and focus into the centre of the forehead.  This allows the next level of super-energy to manifest in the *third-eye chakra* which is perceived as a light.  The light of the third eye chakra appears spontaneously with relaxation and centring of attention.

The focus of attention on each chakra facilitates the opening of the chakras above and allows for super-energy from ever higher levels of the Universe to reach down to the Earth. This brings about the descent of the higher spirit or super-energy self into physicality. Ascension begins with the full integration of the higher super-physical self with the lower hyper-physical self, in the heart of the human being.

Many people think ascension is about leaving the planet when, in fact, it is more about being really centred and present on the planet. Before we ascend, we have to become fully incarnate as a spiritual being. Ascension is the means whereby we complete our cycle of incarnations by being a spiritual as well as a mental, emotional and physical being whilst still on the Earth. This is often described as being fully *grounded*.

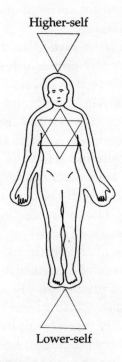

**Higher-self**

**Lower-self**

*Fig. 11.2 Integrating the higher and lower self.*

However, there comes a time when we do have to leave the Earth. Usually this occurs through death of the physical body, but today there are predictions that an alternative to the death process is to be made available to mankind. For those humans who are whole, Loving and caring beings, balanced in body, mind and spirit, there is the possibility of physical ascension.

The possibility of physical ascension is, to my mind, the most significant prediction in the *new science of the spirit*. If the forms of vortex and wave are common to all levels of reality within the Universe, then it should be possible to accelerate the intrinsic speed of energy within every vortex and wave of a body and so cause the body to ascend from the physical to the super-physical realities. This process would not involve any change in the atomic or molecular structure of the body, which means that a living body could ascend the series of quantum realities without disruption in its life processes.

Ascension offers an alternative to the death process by shifting bodies out of physical space-time which controls the ageing and death processes. I believe it is physical ascension, rather than death, that breaks the cycle of birth and death and triggers the return of Life to Source. It is physical ascension which gives us real freedom of the Universe. If physical beings complete their cycles of birth and death and return their Life-strands to their higher-selves, then the higher-selves could return the Life-strands back to the group-selves which could, in turn, return them to the one-self. The return of Life to Source could occur, at the end of each cycle of incarnations, with mass human ascension.

In the new science of the spirit, ascension, as a means of moving bodies in and out of a particular space-time continuum, appears as an obvious prediction. Reversal of the ascension process would make it possible to *descend* bodies of hyper-physical or super-physical reality, back into physical reality. In these ascension or descension processes, bodies would appear or disappear as they step in and out of physical space and time. The processes of ascension and descension could provide an explanation for a host of paranormal phenomena, involving the mysterious appearance and disappearance of physical objects. In *The Vortex: Key to Future Science*, these processes (therein called transubstantiation) were used to explain the *Sai Baba* phenomenon. Sai Baba is an Indian mystic who has the ability to manifest objects at will. He descends psychic objects from his store of memories in the hyper-physical reality, into the physical where they appear as real objects. Geoff Boltwood in England and numerous shamans, world-wide, also have this remarkable ability.

If a body is lifted out of physical space-time by ascension, it can be returned, by descension, to any point in space or time. This could occur anywhere in the physical world and be instantaneous relative to physical space-time. The process of ascension and descension could be used to explain apportation and teleportation phenomena and also accommodate the ever increasing volume of evidence of *extra-terrestrials*.

Whilst modern science has dismissed the possibility that extra-terrestrial craft visit Earth from other planetary systems - on the grounds that space is too vast to be traversed - the ability to move bodies in and out of space-time offers scope for unlimited travel between star systems and galaxies. With the enormous distances between stars and galaxies in the Universe, *intra-space travel* (travel through space) from one planet to another is practically impossible. However, with the feasibility of *inter-space travel* (travel between one space continuum and another) it should be possible to ascend a craft out of the space-time of one planet and descend it into the space-time of another planet. An excellent, conceptual model for inter-space travel is presented in the BBC TV Series, *Dr Who*, with the 'Tardis' as a craft which has the ability to move out of physical space-time and into other spaces and other times. This programme also presents the idea of other intelligent populations existing in the Universe.

We do need to be open to the possibility that we may not be the only intelligent population in the Universe. With hundreds of billions of star systems in the average galaxy and billions of

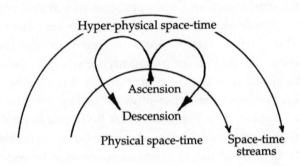

*Fig. 11.3 Inter-space travel*

galaxies in the Universe, not to mention the other realities of which the physical is but a part, there could be *Universal Intelligent Populations (UIPs)* living elsewhere in the Universe. These could be classified as *physical UIPs* and *hyper-physical or super-physical UIPs*. We would qualify as moderately advanced physical UIPs, existing on a small planet, in a modest star system, on the outskirts of the Milky Way galaxy, who have just about made it to the moon by means of crude, gas emission, intra-space travel. More advanced UIPs, employing a superior technology, could reach Earth-space from anywhere in the Universe by means of inter-space travel.

Inter-space travel would also seem to be possible without the employment of craft and technology. Historical records and traditions suggest that the ability to move freely in and out of space-time may be an inherent potential in us all. Apollonius of Tyana is reported to have vanished out of a Roman trial and reappeared, on the same day, in the town of Puteoli, normally three days journey from Rome. Pythagoras was reported to have appeared on the same day to groups of disciples, in towns separated by several hundred miles. In the Christian tradition, Jesus Christ is said to have disappeared and appeared in different places on a number of occasions and in the Islamic tradition,

Mohammed is said to have vanished from Mount Moriah in Jerusalem and reappeared in Mecca.

There are innumerable accounts of native American, African and Australian shamans translocating over vast distances, by disappearing in one place and reappearing in another. For example, in her numerous popular books, Lynn Andrews describes her shamanistic experiences with members of the *Sisterhood of the Shields* who would frequently appear and disappear and thereby translocate themselves instantaneously, between different places.

Mystics from Tibet, India and Japan, have also been reported with the ability to appear and disappear at will and to be masters of the ascension process. For example, Kabir is reported to have appeared in several different places at the same time and both Kabir and Guru Nanak left the Earth by the ascension rather than the death process, a similar story being associated with them both. According to the *Paratan Janamskhi,* on September 7, 1539, as Nanak approached his last moments on Earth an argument broke out amongst his followers. The muslims wanted to bury his body whereas the hindus wanted it cremated. Guru Nanak resolved the argument by telling each group to place flowers alongside his body. Whichever flowers remained fresh after he was gone would indicate which group was to have their own way. He then pulled a sheet over himself. When the sheet was removed only the flowers remained. His body had vanished and all the flowers were fresh. Another Indian guru reported to have ascended was Babaji. In the *Autobiography of a Yogi,* Yogananda referred to Babaji as a 19th-century Indian guru. However, Babaji has reappeared in the 20th century to establish the system of *Rebirthing.* Babaji has achieved a state of physical immortality through ascension and established rebirthing to help others achieve the same state.

On the 23rd June 1974, Kotama Okada, the spiritual leader or *Sukuinushisama* of the Japanese *Mahi Kari* movement, attained physical immortality through the ascension process. He vanished out of the world on that day and since then there have been frequent reports of his appearing all over the world to encourage people to receive the light of Mahi Kari, the system of enlightenment he established.

In the late 19th century, Madame H.P. Blavatsky claimed to have been instructed by the two Indian mahatmas, Koot Humi (Kuthumi) and El Moyra, who had the ability to appear and disappear at will.

According to Frances Hitching, in pre-revolutionary France, the mysterious Count St Germain was also reported to have had the ability to vanish from one place and reappear elsewhere and he never seemed to age. Throughout the period 1723-1789 when he was active in France, he always appeared to be aged between 45-50. His death was recorded on the 27th February 1784 and he was supposed to have been buried on March 2nd at Eckenforde. But he appeared at a conference, in Wilhelmsbad, in 1785 and was active again in France in 1788, warning the nobility of the danger of revolution. He left for Sweden in 1789 and was seen again on the eve of the murder of the Duc de Berri in 1820, when he still appeared to be about 50. Babaji, Kuthumi, El Moyra, and St Germain - to name but a few - now have worldwide recognition as *Ascended Masters*.

The shifting of bodies in and out of space-time and concomitant suspension of the ageing process, is also supposed to have occurred as part of a top secret research programme conducted in America between 1943 and 1983. The project originated from a study of invisibility, in the early 1930s, at the University of Chicago, conducted by Nikola Tesla, Dr Kurtenhauer and Dr J. Hutchinson, Dean of the University. In 1934 the project moved to Princetown for the attention of the newly formed *Institute of Advanced Study* which included Albert Einstein, John Von Newmann and T. Townsend Brown. In 1943, a secret experiment was conducted in Philadelphia harbour, in the course of which a destroyer, the USS Eldridge, is said to have vanished from the harbour of Philadelphia and was reported to have reappeared in the harbour of Norfolk Virginia, several hundred miles away. After World War II the project continued, under the direction of Von Newmann, at the Brookhaven National Laboratory until it was disbanded by Congress in 1967. In *The Montauk Project,* Preston Nichols claims that it was re-established, in 1971, as a secret military project at the Montauk Airforce Base on Long Island. He reports that by 1983 the research team had *teleportation beams* in full and successful operation by means of which they were manifesting thoughtforms as physical objects and projecting people in and out of physical space-time.

Inter-space travel by means of teleportation beams has been dramatised as "Beam me up Scotty" in the American television series *Startrek* and I believe it could be teleportation beams, operated from the fifth quantum reality, that will bring about the mass ascension of humanity, before the year 2012. I envisage that those who choose to be involved in physical ascension will perceive the end of the teleportation beam as an opening of light and experience the beam as a vortex tunnel. In order to partake in the ascension process all the individual has to do is step into the *doorway of light.* I imagine that within the teleportation beam, connecting our space-time to that of the fifth quantum reality, the speed of energy in every particle of the ascending body will be accelerated beyond the speed of light. This process, as I have described it, should not involve changes in the atomic or molecular structure of the body. There would be no dematerialising or vapourising, nor would there be an increase in the frequency of vibration of the energy in the body - an increase in the frequency of vibration in matter would result in a temperature increase that would be fatal to living organisms. My prediction for the ascension of physical bodies suggests a process that would be perfectly safe for living organisms. Whilst I do not know the precise technology, I suspect it involves super-energy resonance.

The possibility of humans ascending on mass offers an extraordinary test for my second prediction. Their subsequent descent from higher quantum realities, with the ability to repeat the ascent and descent of matter in the laboratory under experimental test conditions, would verify my first prediction.

According to a number of sources, the Earth itself is destined to ascend into the fifth level of reality before the year 2013. Predictions of the ascension of the Earth may be speculative but I support them - they do, after all, offer the ultimate test for the vortex hypothesis.

My way of accounting for the ascension of the Earth is based upon the speculation that the solar system is situated in a *zone of density* in which the speed of energy is depressed to that of common light. (I am of the opinion that the speed of light is not uniform throughout the Universe. I believe that the speed of energy in many stars and planetary systems is much faster than the speed of common light as we measure it on Earth. Each star system could be in zone which governs the speed of its energy. As energy moves or extends from one zone to another its speed would increase or decrease according to the underlying nature of the zone. I call the energy speed-zone we live in a zone of density because I consider the speed of energy within it to be depressed to a comparatively low level.) As light from other stars enters our zone of density, its speed would be depressed so that we measure it to be uniform - the same velocity as the velocity of light from the Sun. (The effect of this situation on time would provide an account for the anomaly that the age of planets in our solar system - as estimated by Einstein - is greater than that of the Universe.)

The ancients believed that they were looking into Heaven as they viewed the stars in the night sky. Perhaps they were right! It could be that many of the stars in the sky are hyper-physical or even super-physical. When they spoke of a *fall in grace* for our planet, could it be that they were referring to a fall in the intrinsic speed of energy in our world? Were they attempting to explain that in the distant past, our solar system became contained in its present zone of density which caused a fall in the speed of its energy? The predicted ascension of the Earth could be the reversal of this situation. The displacement of a star system from a zone of density would cause the speed of energy in every particle of matter and photon of light to revert to a higher value - which would correspond to its ascension

I believe that the Universe is a living being and that zones of density correspond to its immune system. Intelligent organisms on planetary systems, bent on war and greed and plunder for resources, correspond - in my opinion - to pathogens and parasites. Zones of density would act to isolate star systems infected with such disease organisms, to prevent their spread to other planetary systems. The removal of a planetary system from quarantine in a zone of density would obviously only occur after planets within the system have been completely cleansed of the infective organism. This would correspond to the great Earth changes that have been predicted to occur just prior to the ascension.

Whether these events come to pass or not is impossible to say. At the time of writing they are merely predictions and speculations. However, it cannot be denied that our world is in a critical state. What good are science and religions that have become hopelessly dull, bogged down in complexity, torn in conflict, and locked in entrenched attitudes whilst the Earth around is dying? There is a need, as never before, for a fresh approach to science and the spirit which will renew hope and unify these two areas of greatest human aspiration.

# Bibliography

I thank following publishers for kind permission to take quotes from the  publications listed below:

**Andrews,** Lynn V., *Flight of the Seventh Moon* (1984), Routledge & Kegan Paul.

**Alexandersson,** Olaf, *Living Water:* Viktor Schauberger and the Secrets of Natural Energy (1990), Gateway Books.

**Ash,** David, *The Tower of Truth* (1977), Camspress.

**Ash,** David & **Hewitt,** Peter *Science of the Gods,* now *The Vortex: Key to Future Science* (1990), Gateway Books, Wellow, Bath, UK.

**Ash,** David & Heather, *Activation for Ascension* (1995), Kima Global Publishers, PO Box 374, Rondebosch 7700, South Africa.

**Argüelles,** Josè, The Mayan Factor (1987), Bear & Co.

**Berkson,** William, *Fields of Force* (1974), Routledge and Kegan Paul.

**Blavatsky** H.P., *The Secret Doctrine*, Theosophical Society.

**Bohm,** David, *Wholeness and the Implicate Order* (1983), Ark.

**Burr,** Harold Saxton, *Blueprint for Immortality: The Electrical Patterns of Life* (1977), Neville Spearman.

**Calder,** Nigel, *Key to the Universe: A Report on the New Physics* (1977) & *Einstein's Universe* (1979), BBC Publications.

**Capra,** Fritjof, *The Turning Point* (1983), Fontana.

**Clerk,** R.W., *Einstein: His Life and Times* (1973), Hodder & Stoughton.

**Clerk-Maxwell,** James, *Scientific Papers*, Vol. ii (1890).

**Deutsche-Physik,** No.7, Morellenfeldgasse 16, A-8010 Graz, Austria.

**Dowding** Lord, Extract from speech on vivisection in the House of Lords, reprinted from Hansard by kind permission of H.M.Stationery Office.

**Feynman,** Richard (with **Leighton & Sands**), *The Feynman Lectures on Physics* (1963), Addison Wesley.

**Feynman,** Richard, *The Character of Physical Law* (1965), BBC Publications. With introduction by Paul Davies (1992), Penguin.

**Fritzsh,** Harald, *Quarks: The Stuff of Matter* (1983), Allen Lane.

**Gamow,** George, *Thirty Years that Shook Physics*, Heinemann.

**Gleick,** James, *Chaos* (1988), William Heinemann Ltd.

**Good,** Timothy, *Above Top Secret* (1987), Sidgwick & Jackson.

**Harvey,** Andrew, *Hidden Journey* (1991), Rider.

**Hawking,** Stephen, *A Brief History of Time* (1988), Bantam Press.

**Hawking,** Stephen, *Black Holes and Baby Universes* and Other Essays (1993), Bantam Books.

**Heisengerg,** Werner, *Physics and Philosophy* (1958), *Across Frontiers* (1974), Harper & Row.

**Hitching,** Frances, *The World Atlas of Mysteries* (1979), Pan Books.

**Hoffmann,** Banesh, *The Strange Story of the Quantum* (1963), Penguin.

**Hoyle,** Sir Fred, *The Intelligent Universe* (1983), Michael Joseph.

**Hurtak,** James, *The Keys of Enoch* (1973),The Academy for Future Science, PO Box F.E.,Los Gatos, CA 95031, USA.

**Icke,** David, *The Robots' Rebellion* (1994), Gateway Books.

**Klein,** Eric, *The Crystal Stair: A Guide to the Ascension* (1992), Oughten House Publications.

**Kuhn,** Thomas, *The Structure of Scientific Revolutions* (1970), *The Essential Tension: Selected Studies in Scientific Tradition and Change* (1977), University of Chicago Press.

**Leggett,** A.J., *The Problems of Physics* (1987), Oxford University Press.

**Matthews,** Robert, *Unravelling the Mind of God* (1992), Virgin Books.

**Mason,** Peggy & **Laing,** Ron, *Sai Baba, The Embodiment of Love* (1993), Gateway Books.

**McKenzie,** A.E., *A Second (MKS) Course in Electricity* (1968), Cambridge University Press.

**Mind Alive Encyclopedia:** *Basic Science,* Marshall Cavendish

**Moody,** Raymond, *Life after Life* (1967), Bantam Books.

**Nelkon & Parker,** *Advanced Level Physics* (1982), Methuen.

**Newman,** Joseph Westley, *The Energy Machine of Joseph Newman* (1986) - Joseph Newman, Route 1, Box 52, Lucedale, Mississippi 39452, USA.

**Nichols,** B.Preston, *The Montauk Project* (1992), Sky Books.

**Pagels,** Heinz, *The Cosmic Code* (1982), Michael Joseph.

**Popper,** Karl, *The Logic of Scientific Discovery* (1968), Hutchinson.

**Ramacharaka ,**Yogi, *An Advanced Course in Yogi Philosophy* (1904), Fowler.

**Rho,** Sigma, *Ether Technology: A Rational Approach to Gravity Control* (1977), Rho Sigma publication.

**Richards, Sears, Wehr & Zemansky,** *Modern University Physics* (1973), Addison-Wesley.

**Russell,** Edward, *Design for Destiny* (1971), Neville Spearman.

**Schrödinger,** Erwin, *Science and Humanism* (1951), Cambridge University Press.

**Segre,** Emilio, *Nuclei & Particles* (1964), Benjamin Inc.

**Sheldrake,** Rupert, *A New Science of Life* (1987), Paladin Books.

**Steiger,** Brad & **Bielek** Alfred, *The Philadelphia Experiment,* Inner Light.

**Steiner,** Rudolf, *Theosophy* (1922), Rudolf Steiner Press.

**Thompson,** S.P., *Life of Lord Kelvin* (1910), Macmillan.

**Thomson,** J.J., *Treatise on the Motion of Vortex Rings* (1884), University of Cambridge.

**Thomson,** William (Lord Kelvin), *Mathematical & Physical Papers* (1841 -1882), 6 vols.

**Watson,** James, *The Double Helix* (1974), Penguin Books.

**Wynniatt,** C.B., Report on Searl's conviction in Letters to the Editor, *Energy Unlimited* (1986), Issue 20.

**Yogananda,** Paramahansa, *The Autobiography of a Yogi* (1987), Rider.

**Zukav,** Gary, *The Dancing Wu Li Masters* (1979), Rider.

# Index